VOLUME 2

HYDRANGEAS

SPECIES & CULTIVARS

Illustrations on cover pages :
Front : *Hydrangea macrophylla ' Renate Steiniger'.*
Back : *Vauville botanical garden.*

ACKNOWLEDGEMENTS

The author and the publisher express their heartfelt thanks to the people whose names appear below, all of whom have contributed in one way or another, by their talent, their knowledge or their support, towards bringing this book into existence. Both author and publisher wish to take this opportunity to convey their gratitude and friendship to all of them.

Claude BELLION - Robert de BOSMELET - Corinne BOULENGER - Micheline BOUSQUET Mark BROWN - Mrs. BULLIVANT - Gwenaëlle CAPRON - Raymond CLARYSSE - Paul and Bénédicte CORTIER - Jelena and Robert DE BELDER - Jean-Louis DANTEC - Jean-Pierre DEMOLY - Ken DURIO - Paul DUSSINE - Maurice DUSSINE - Emmanuel GUIBERT - Maurice and Rosemary FOSTER - Kiyoshi FUJII - Noboru FUJIOKA - J.M. GARDINER - Jacques de GIVRY - Tetsu and Kumiko HIRASAWA - Mariko HOSHINO - Jean-Claude JOLINON - Marguerite KAMMER - Mototeru KAMO - Renaud de KERCHOVE - Yuji KURASHIGE - Olivier LANCESSEUR - Yves et Gloria LE BELLEGARD - Martine and Francis LEMMONIER - Yolande LONGUEMARE - Solange LOUVET Jacqueline MALLET - Victoria MATTHEWS - Sylvester MARSH - Elizabeth McCLINTOCK Pierre François MICHEL-KERNEUR - Mariko MOLIA - Jacques NEILZ - Margherita PACCALIN Arabella and Jean-Bernard OUVRIEU - Kazuyo and Masaaki OZAKI - Alain RENOUF Members of the Shamrock Association - Hiroshi SHIMIZU - Greta STURDZA - Takaaki SUGIMOTO Dr L.A. TJON SIE FAT - Harry van TRIER - Yvonne de VAUCORBEIL - Bryan WOY Takeomi YAMAMOTO - Tomohisa YUKAWA.

The original French version of this book appeared in October 1994.
This English version was translated by Bryan Woy.

ISBN 2 - 9506523 - 4 - 4 (Whole publication)
ISBN 2 - 9506523 - 6 - 0 (Vol. 2)

HYDRANGEAS

SPECIES & CULTIVARS

Corinne Mallet

CONTENTS

to Takeomi Yamamoto,
with great respect.

INTRODUCTION

The genus *Hydrangea* is so important and extensive that a complete inventory is called for, with published descriptions of all the large number of different cultivars and species which are at present known and conserved.

The purpose of the first volume[1] of "Hydrangeas, species and cultivars"* was to serve as an introduction to the genus for the general reader and also to make it better known to both botanical and horticultural professionals.

The favourable response we have received from readers around the world has confirmed the value of the first volume, but many lesser-known plants remained to be described, and this is what we have endeavoured to do in the present volume.

It would not be possible to deal with the genus at full length in this second volume, mainly because of the disappearance (temporary, we hope) of many cultivars of *Hydrangea macrophylla* and also because of the difficulty of studying living specimens of some species which have never been cultivated (mostly in the *Cornidia* section, which consists essentially of South American members of the *Hydrangea* genus). We hope, however, that this book will fill in a number of gaps in the knowledge of the genus.

There can be no doubt that interest in these magnificent plants will never end, for old cultivars are being rediscovered all the time, and new ones created. With regard to this, it should be pointed out that the private plant collections grouped together under such bodies as the CCVS[2] in France or the NCCPG[3] in the United Kingdom are a real biological treasure house ; the public authorities should realize that such collections are of equal importance with national botanical gardens, and encourage the creation and upkeep of these national resources. Together with water, sun and soil, plants are the basis of life on earth ; let us hope that both love and knowledge of plants will continue to grow during years to come.

(1) Originally published in French with the title 'Hortensias et autres *Hydrangea*'
(2) CCVS : Conservatoire des collections végétales spécialisées.
(3) NCCPG : National Council for the Conservation of Plants and Gardens.
* Asterisks in Volume 2 refer to entries in Volume 1.

CLASSIFICATION OF SPECIES IN THIS BOOK

FAMILY	Hydrangeaceae						
GENUS	HYDRANGEA						
SECTIONS	Hydrangea					Cornidia	
SUB-SECTIONS	Americanae	Asperae	Petalanthe	Heteromallae	Macrophyllae	Monosegia	Polysegia
SPECIES	quercifolia	sikokiana involucrata aspera	hirta scandens	paniculata heteromalla	macrophylla serrata	integrifolia	serratifolia

CHAPTER 1

HISTORICAL NOTES

Biography of
Philipp Franz von Siebold

European cultivars

Portrait of Philipp Franz von Siebold
by Emmanuel Guibert.

HISTORICAL NOTES

The introducer

All lovers of hydrangeas and of Japanese flora are familiar with the name of Philipp Franz von Siebold. In the first half of the 19th century, this remarkable man, a physician who became a botanist, spent two long periods in Japan, where he developed a great love for the country and its wildlife. He was the author of a beautiful "Flora Japonica" and became the greatest expert of his time on Japanese hydrangeas. He created a botanical garden and nursery from where he distributed throughout Europe examples of the many plants he had collected during his journeys, including many hydrangeas. He was described as being "surrounded by a kind of aura", and was the first real representative of Japanese hydrangeas in Europe.

The creators of Hydrangea macrophylla

The French were the first to use *Hydrangea macrophylla* for cross-fertilization and breeding from seed, working from examples introduced by such great importers of plants as Philipp Franz von Siebold and James Veitch. Horticulturalists from the rest of Europe were, however, not slow to catch them up.

As early as 1913, a German, J. Wintergalen, introduced his *H. m.* 'Westfalen Kind'. Although the First World War slowed down the activities of plant breeders, the inter-war period was one of great invention, producing so many new cultivars that it would be impossible to list them all. After World War II, French horticulture was reduced to almost nothing, particularly in the field of hydrangeas ; on the other hand, this period saw a spectacularly rapid expansion in the production of new *Hydrangea macrophylla* cultivars in the rest of Europe, which went on until the 1980s. Since then, it seems that the large majority of plant breeders have abandoned *Hydrangea macrophylla* in favour of other species such as *H. paniculata* and *H. quercifolia*.

It nevertheless seems possible that in the near future, the Japanese cultivars of this species which have only just been imported to the West will create a renewal of interest in *Hydrangea macrophylla*.

BIOGRAPHY OF PHILIPP FRANZ VON SIEBOLD

Translation of a short biography in French by Hortulanus Witte which appeared in the Catalogue des Etablissements d'Introduction de Plantes du Japon et de Chine, cultivées dans le Jardin d'Acclimatation de Feu Monsieur Philipp Franz von Siebold (the catalogue of von Siebold's botanical garden and plant nursery) in Leiden (Holland) in 1867.

To correspondents of the Establishment of the late Monsieur Ph. F. von Siebold at Leiden.

We have to repeat the sad news, which since last October has spread through the horticultural world as well as the world of scholars : the death of Monsieur le Chevalier von Siebold.

On the 18th October 1866 a short illness put an end to the life of this scholarly and energetic man, to whom botany and horticulture owe so much recognition.

It is not at all our intention to publish his biography here. It would be impossible to recount in this short preface a life of seventy years which was active above all else ; that would require an entire volume. In addition, we hardly doubt that more skilful hands than ours will undertake this extensive task ; however we would not have wished to begin the new catalogue of the establishment founded by him - the first not edited by his own hand - without devoting a few words to the memory of this man, so renowned throughout Europe, whose very name deserves higher praise than we are capable of giving.

PHILIPP FRANZ VON SIEBOLD was German, born in Würzburg on the 17th February 1797, into a family several of whose members had achieved great merit in medical science. He received a meticulous education in that town, and achieved the grade of doctor in 1820.

Two years later, he enlisted with the military service of the Dutch East India Company as a medical officer, and when the Dutch Government later organized a scientific mission to Japan, he took part both as a doctor and as a natural historian.

It was there that he expanded his activities so as to learn about all the characteristics of that country (which had been closed until then to all European nations), so as to study the habits and customs of the inhabitants and, at the same time, so as to collect together the objects and documents relevant to his studies. Such work as this may be equalled, but can never be surpassed. Evident proof of this may be found in his rich collection, which is now the property of the Dutch Government and comprises the major part of the Leiden Ethnographical Museum ; in a number of works on the customs, habits, language, etc. of the Japanese ; and on the flora of that country, etc.

He returned to the Netherlands in October 1830 and, although he kept the rank of Colonel in the staff of the Dutch army in the East Indies, he left the military service to devote all his time to arranging his collection of Japanese objects and, later, to organizing and directing his establishment for the cultivation of plants from Japan.

In 1859, at an already advanced age, he made a second journey to Japan, that country for which he had such a marked predilection, and once again collected not only a great number of plants, which he grew in a special garden in Edo so as to be able to later transport them to Europe, but also a second collection of ethnographical objects ; this collection was purchased some time ago by H. M. the King of Bavaria and is destined for the museum in Munich.

During the last years of his life he spent almost all his time in Germany, either in Bonn, where he then lived with his family, or in Munich, where he was continuously occupied with the arrangement of his new collections ; it was while engaged in this that death struck him down at the age of 70.

Eloquent witnesses to his achievement are, firstly in the field of botany, particularly with regard to the Japanese flora, the "Flora Japonica", written by him in collaboration with Prof. Zuccarini, and a large number of other botanical writings ; and secondly in the field of horticulture, his establishment for the introduction of plants from Japan and China and the resulting distribution of a great number of beautiful plants which are now, and in some cases have already been for several years, the ornament of many a European garden or greenhouse.

In 1844 he founded this establishment near Leiden, which is now known and reputed as far as the most distant frontiers of Europe, where he cultivated all that he had collected of the flora of Japan, and which was continuously increased by plants and seeds that were ceaselessly sent to him from that country. His local knowledge of this beautiful land and its rich flora enabled him to inform his correspondents in Japan of the places where they should search for the plants which he wished to introduce to Europe.

We should nevertheless be aware that his establishment was in no way a speculation, but rather the result of an ardent desire to introduce to Europe everything which seemed to him to be worthy of interest, whether from the botanical, medical, economic or technical point of view, or simply as ornamental plants for horticulture ; his disinterested goal was to be useful to industry. Then again, consignments of plants sent at great expense sometimes gave very unsatisfactory results, either because of lack of care in packing of because of the length of the journey, and it will be readily understood that all this cost him a great deal of money which he was not able to recoup from the activities of his establishment. This enterprise was thus a genuine sacrifice made to science and to horticulture, a fact which is generally too little known.

Despite this, his zeal never slackened, and he continued to introduce new plants right up until the last year of his life. The new plants listed in this new catalogue serve as proof of his love for the flora of Japan, of which he never spoke without great enthusiasm.

In addition, one only has to glance at the various catalogues written by him, even while in the country of his dreams, to realize to what extent he was steeped in Japanese plant lore. It is above all the catalogue and price list of plants and seeds from Japan and China grown in this establishment, which contains a note on the state of horticulture in Japan and the importance of everyday and ornamental plants cultivated in his establishment in Leiden, that contains some of the most instructive features. As late as 1866 he published an extract of the catalogue, printed in Munich, containing some most interesting observations about the plants of Japan, which provides ample proof that his zeal and energy did not diminish with age.

And what is now to become of this establishment that he loved so dearly, so much so that he always regretted that his many occupations only rarely allowed him to stay here ?
The answer requires few words, and it is a great pleasure to be able to communicate it to all those who are interested : it will continue to function in the same way and with the same resources as before, as far as this is possible without the powerful protection of its founder. Madame von Siebold, his widow, could think of no better way of honouring his memory than to continue to operate an institution for which he had so much affection, and we ourselves willingly took on the task of writing this new catalogue, which gives us the opportunity to pay homage to the memory of a man who gave us proof of his friendship on several occasions, and whose memory will linger on in us and all those who knew him and appreciated his disinterested enthusiasm for spreading knowledge about the flora of one of the most beautiful countries in the world.

Leiden, 10th January 1867

H.WITTE
Chief Gardener of the Botanical Garden
of Leiden University

European cultivars

(for French cultivars, see Volume 1)

1914 - 1987

G. Arends, (Wuppertal) Germany.
1961 : 'Preziosa'

D. Baardse, (Aalsmeer) Holland.
1915 : 'John Van Den Berg', 'Hortulanus Witte',
     'La France', 'Madame de Vries', 'Mignon'
1918 : 'John C. Mensing', 'Mrs. Baardse'
1920 : **'Baardse's Favourite'**, 'Queen Emma'
1921 : 'Deutschland', 'Princesse Juliana'
1922 : 'Bagatelle', 'Königin Wilhemina'
1924 : 'Jonkheer Van Den Tetz'
1927 : 'Colonel Lindbergh'
1930 : 'Aalsmeer's Glory'
No date : 'Hollandia'

Willi Binz Kg., (Rastatt) Germany.
No date : 'Edith Binz'

Brugger, (Tettnang) Germany.
1946 : **'Montfort Perle'**
1951 : **'Ave Maria'**
No date : **'Merkur'**

Michael Haworth-Booth, (Farall - Surrey) England.
No date : **'Violetta'**, **'Blue Deckle'**

Emil Draps, (Strombeek) Belgium.
1935 : 'Miss Belgium'
1938 : 'Charming', 'Drap's pink', 'King George',
     'Leopold III', **'Mme G.F. de Bier'**,
     'Mme J.de Smedt', **'Président R.Touchard'**,
1946 : 'Princesse Béatrice'

Draps-Dom, (Strombeek) Belgium.
1950 : 'Raymond Draps', 'Splendeur'
1956 : 'King George VII'
No date : 'Armand Draps', 'Land Express'
syn. 'La Lande'

Dieneman, Germany.
1962 : 'Herman Dieneman' syn.'Leuchtfeuer'

Fischer, (Wiesbaden) Germany.
1930 : **'Fischers Silberblau'**

P. Flores, (Wuppertal-Sonnenborn) Germany.
1931 : 'Edelweiss'

E. Haller, (Brugg) Switzerland.
1960 : 'Brunegg', 'Habsburg', **'Schenkenberg'**
1964 : 'Besserstein', 'Altenburg'
1965 : 'Tindonissa'
1966 : 'Freudenstein', 'Schwan'
1967 : 'Lenzburg', 'Wildegg', 'Kastelu'
1968 : 'Ostergruss'
1969 : 'Hallwyl'
1970 : 'Biberstein', **'Liebegg'**, 'Trostburg',
     'Wildenstein'
1971 : 'Böttstein', **'Brugg'**, **'Tegerfelden'**
1972 : 'Brestenberg'
1974 : **'Aarburg'**, **'Horben'**
1975 : Burg Rosenberg', 'Bellikon', 'Burg Königstein'
1978 : 'Stein', 'Wartburg', **'Goffersberg'**, 'Thierstein',
     'Heidegg', 'Iberg'

J.P. Hartmann, (Ghent) Belgium.
1935 : 'Sigyn Hartmann'

Gijseling, Belgium.
No date: 'Floralia' (1960 ?), 'Mme Aimé Gijseling'

H. J. Jones, (according to Mr. Haworth-Booth).
England.
1921 : 'W.J. Hepburn'
1927 : 'Archie Mowbray', 'David Igamelis',
     'Duchess of York', 'H. B May', 'H.J. Jones',
     'Highland glory', 'Jubilee', 'J.F.McLeod',
     'King George','Lord Lambourne',
     'Miss Phyllis Cato', 'Mrs. Alice Blandy',
     'Mrs. A. Simmonds', 'Mrs. Chas. Davis'

F. K. Kluis.
1932 : **'Kluis Superba'**
1945 : 'Kluis Superior'
No date : **'Kluis Sensation'**

F. Matthes.
1923 : **'Goliath'**
1924 : 'Marie Matthes'
1925 : **'Blauer Prinz'**
1926 : **'Gartenbaudirektor Kuhnhert'**
1928 : **'Zukunft'**
1929 : **'Heinrich Seidel'**
1931 : 'Fortschritt'
No date: 'Schöne Dresdnerin' syn. 'Beauty of Dresden',

Note : Cultivars described in Volumes 1 and 2 are in bold type.

'Friedrich Matthes', 'Mein Liebling',
'Gertrude Glahn', 'Graf Zeppelin', 'Hortus',
'Sachsenkind', 'St.Bonifaz', 'Spätsommer'

Gebrüder Moll, (Erben - Zürich) Switzerland.
1934 : **'Regula'**
1946 : 'Carl Spitteler', 'C.F. Meyer', 'Felix',
        'Gottfried Keller'
1947 : 'Zürich'
No date : 'Auckmann', 'Wiesbaden'

Nieschütz, Germany.
No date : 'Nymphe'

H. Schadendorff, Germany.
1928 : 'Schadendorff's Perle'
1929 : 'Elbe'
1931 : 'Altona' syn. 'Althone', **'Europa'**, **'Hamburg'**
No date: Frühlingserwachen', **'Holstein'**

Steiniger, (Lemmenhof - Tönisvorst)
Germany.
1951 : **'Vorster Frührot'**
1956 : **'Elmar Steiniger'**
1957 : **'Adria'**, 'Sensation 75' syn.'**Harlequin'**
1964 : **'Renate Steiniger'**
1965 : **'Blauer Zwerg'**
1979 : **'Sontagskind'**
1980 : **'Eugen Hahn'**
No date : 'Abendrot', 'Dr.Bernhard Steiniger', 'Hera',
'Iris', **'Mathilda Gütges'**, 'Marmor Prinzessin',
'Morgenrot', **'Sibilla'**, 'Steina 104', 'Schwester Alba',
'Sonja Steiniger', **'Weisse Königin'**

James Veitch & Son, England.
1879 : 'Mariesii'
1899 : 'Rosea'
No date : 'Veitchii'(1881 ?)

K. Wezelenburg, Germany.
1914 : **'Niedersachsen'**,
1927 : 'Baroness Shröder', 'Colonel Durham',
'D.B. Crane', 'Florence Bolt', 'Queen Mary', 'Mesdag'

1928 : 'Frans Hals'
1936 : 'Edison', 'Joseph Israels', 'Jupiter', 'Marconi',
        'Mars', 'Rubens', 'Venus', 'Jan Steen'
1937 : 'Covent Garden', 'Münster'

J. Wintergalen, (Münster) Germany.
1913 : 'Westfalen Kind'
1917 : 'Osting'
1920 : **'Lancelot'**, 'Rheingold'
1921 : 'Peer Gynt', 'Helge'
1922 : **'Parzifal'**
1923 : 'Gudrun'
1924 : 'Krimhild', 'Lorelei'
1926 : 'Siegfried'
1928 : 'Elmar', 'Freya'
1930 : 'Tosca'
1932 : 'Odin', Wiking'
1933 : 'Nixe'
1934 : 'Meteor'
1937 : 'Daphné'
1938 : 'Carmen'
1940 : **'Westfalen'**
1943 : 'Joseph Wintergalen'
No date: 'Giselher', 'Pasteur', 'Sieger',
Swanhild'

E.F.A, (Wädenswil) Switzerland.
1947 : 'Etzel', 'Bachtel'
1949 : 'Säntis'
1951 : 'Albis'
1952 : 'Hörnli', **'Tödi'**
1960 : 'Pilatus', **'Rigi'**
1964 : 'Drusberg', 'Glärnisch', **'Libelle'**, 'Möwe',
        'Mythen'
1968 : **'Nachtigall'**
1979 : **'Blaumeise'**, **'Eisvogel'**, **'Fasan'**, **'Mücke'**,
        'Rotkelchen', **'Taube'**, **'Zaunkönig'**, 'Zeisig'
1983 : **'Elster'**, 'Pfau'
1984 : **'Blaüling'**
1987 : **'Bachstelze'**, 'Bergfink', 'Blaukehlchen',
        'Buchfink', 'Buntspecht', 'Flamingo',
        'Gimpel', 'Grasmüke', **'Kardinal'**, 'Papagei',
        'Rotdrossel', **'Rotschwanz'**

Note : Cultivars described in Volumes 1 and 2 are in bold type.

COLOUR SERIES

CHAPTER 2

WESTERN CULTIVARS
of *Hydrangea macrophylla*

WHITE

'AVE MARIA' : Brugger, 1951. Certainly the freshest-looking white *Hydrangea macrophylla* of the "hortensia" type. A great profusion of small, compact "mop-head" inflorescences, 11-12 cm across. Sterile florets, about 3.5 cm wide, are composed of 4 restrained, regular sepals with d enticulate edges. A second flowering is possible in favourable years. As the flowers take a long time to turn white, it is certainly the greenest-looking variety of all, a fact which makes it useful for setting off other plants in a garden. Rarely grows taller than 100 cm. Compact and vigorous growth, but susceptible to chlorosis and burning if planted in full sunlight. Should only be grown in rich, acid soil. Sheltered regions. Illustration n° 1, page 25

'BACHSTELZE' : Wädenswill, 1987. This cultivar is sometimes wrongly called 'Kwikstaartje' in Dutch and 'Wagtail' in English. It is a member of the "Teller" series, and has a "blood" relationship with both 'Tödi'* and 'Libelle'*, from the latter of which it has inherited white sterile florets in single or double rows. Sepals are entire or slightly denticulate, and the fertile flowers are blue. Inflorescences are 18 cm across. Compact habit, like its ancestor 'Tödi'. Maximum height of about 120 cm when mature. It is moderately hardy, and flowers towards the middle of the season, sometimes with a second flowering. A fine, frosty white, the plant is seen to its full advantage when grown in a shady position in coastal regions. Illustration n° 4, page 26.

'BICHON' : Dublanchet, year unknown. A magnificent green-washed white, it will sometimes produce a second show of flowers even though it is late flowering. The round, compact "mop-head" inflorescences are made up of sterile florets with from 3 to 5 wide, irregular sepals, entire or very slightly dentate, with beak-shaped ends. It is used a great deal in forcing as, in addition to producing large numbers of flowers, it stands up very straight. Unfortunately it is subject to pest damage and may not flower at all when it has been attacked the previous year. The plant has handsome green, shiny foliage and can grow to a height of 160 cm in the right

conditions. Unlike most white hydrangeas, the flowers are quite resistant to rain. Suitable for all regions. Illustration n° 7, page 26.

'ELSTER' : Wädenswill, 1983. The name means "Magpie".It is also wrongly called 'Ekster' in Dutch. A plant in the "Teller" series with very large, extremely graceful inflorescences. Sterile florets have 3 or 4 entire sepals that are of irregular width and clearly detached from one another ; this gives a very light effect to the inflorescences, which can be up to 20 cm across. The colour is between white and blue, and brings delicate bone china to mind. There are many large, decorative fertile flowers, coloured a fine cerulean blue, at the centre of the inflorescence. Foliage is dark green, very shiny, with oval acuminate leaves. The shrub is of upright habit, reaching a height of about 100 cm when mature. It is relatively hardy, but sensitive to spring frosts. For mild regions. Illustration n° 5, page 26.

'LOUIS MOUILLERE' : Emile Mouillère, 1920. A cultivar which has almost been forgotten, but which is among the most interesting whites produced by Emile Mouillère. Inflorescences are of the "hortensia" type, about 15 cm wide, and are uneven in both form and colour, as the sterile florets from which they are formed mature at different times ; some are already pure white while other younger ones are still greenish or yellowish white. The florets have from 3 to 5 unevenly fimbriate sepals about 2 cm long which are rhomboid or oval in shape. Leaves are bifid or trifid, coloured a uniform mid-green, fairly large and very healthy. A very distinctive plant, well worth growing. Suitable for all regions. Illustration n° 8, page 26.

'NYMPHE' : Nieschütz, year unknown. An early-flowering plant, with inflorescences in the form of hemispheres 18 cm wide, made up of pure white sterile florets with four regular, deeply denticulate sepals ; these are very wide, separate from one another at the base, sometimes mottled with green and becoming dotted with pink and red as flowering goes on. It has beautiful rounded shiny leaves, clear green, with an undulate surface and deeply dentate edges. Flowering is abundant, often with a second show of flowers, but unfortunately very sensitive to rain, which will turn the flowers rusty straight away. It is a compact, upright plant, and a consistent and prolific flowerer, but should only be grown in regions where rainfall is not too high, or else used for forcing. Maximum height 120 cm. A good plant for cut flowers, as inflorescences will stay looking fresh for over ten days. Illustration n° 2, page 25.

'REGULA' : Moll, 1934. A shrub with broad, white, "hortensia" type inflorescences that can grow up to 20 cm wide, made up of sterile florets over 6 cm wide with round, entire sepals. This prolific shrub grows vigorously, with abundant healthy foliage and strong woody parts, and it is one of the greatest successes produced by German breeders. It is very resistant to disease and, although an excellent plant for forcing, it does very well in the open, where it can be seen to full advantage. Mature height 100 cm. An absolute must ; well worth trying. Suitable for all regions. Illustration n° 3, page 25.

'SIR JOSEPH BANKS' : Although presented as being the plant brought from China by Joseph Banks in 1789, the cultivar grown under this name is not at all like the dried specimen in the herbarium put together by Banks and kept in the British Museum. Be that as it may, this cultivar has very large spherical inflorescences, 25 cm wide, which are white washed with pink or mauve. Sterile florets are small, with 4 entire sepals that do not overlap. These become dotted with carmine late in the season, in a similar way to *H. m.* 'Mme Emile Mouillère'. Woody parts are strong and foliage is healthy. The fertile flowers hidden inside the inflorescences are very interesting, for they are among the largest of the species, and the different parts can easily be examined with a magnifying glass. The shrub is late-flowering, and can grow over 200 cm tall when mature. It is sensitive to cold, particularly spring frosts, so should only be grown in a mild climate. Illustration n° 6, page 26.

'WEISSE KÖNIGIN' : Steiniger, 1980 The name means "White Queen". This plant is widely used for forcing, but is perfectly suitable for growing in the open. A distinctive feature of the "hortensia" type inflorescences is that they are oval rather than round ; one side of the base is longer than the other, the two elliptical axes being 19 cm and 12 cm. Their colour is a fine white speckled with green, and they stand out well against the rounded leaves, which are a handsome dark green. Another characteristic of the plant is that the stems have a very fine grainy surface instead of the usual lenticels or pores. Unlike other varieties of *Hydrangea macrophylla*, the sterile florets and fertile flowers are completely white throughout. Suitable for all regions except those with a very severe climate. Illustration n° 9, page 26.

BLUE

'ADRIA' : August Steiniger, 1957. The name means "Adriatic". This plant has hemispherical inflorescences of a fine blue, although they take on a poorer colour as they age. It is highly suitable for forcing, but is, unfortunately, only seldom grown in gardens. It is of compact habit, and flowering is abundant and dependable. The inflorescences, 18 cm across, are tightly-packed and formed from sterile florets with 4 or 5 entire sepals which are slightly wavy, with tips the shape of a teapot spout. The broad-toothed leaves are small, shiny, rounded and sharply acuminate. Excellent for dried flower arrangements. Mature height around 1 metre. Suitable for all regions. Illustration n° 10, page 27.

'ARDTORNISH' : A selection bred in the garden of Ardtornish in Scotland. this plant resembles the cultivar 'Frillibet' *, but with more inflorescences of a smaller size. Also the stems are suppler, giving it a weeping appearance when it flowers. Sterile florets are made up of light, denticulate sepals which grow at different levels and give a tousled look to the flower heads. Inflorescences are about 14 cm wide, and a fine light blue, becoming tinged with green late in the season. They are unevenly distributed on the bush and are well suited for use in cut flower arrangements. The general appearance of the plant is irresistibly coquettish. Foliage is mid-green. Mature height 120 cm. Suitable for all regions. Illustration n° 11, page 27.

'BLAUER ZWERG' : August Steiniger, 1965. The name means "Blue Dwarf". A cultivar also known by the erroneous names 'Lavblau' or 'Lavender Blue'. A fine, upright plant producing prolific quantities of small purplish-blue "mop-heads", which are formed from florets with 5 small, entire, almond-shaped sepals. The stems are strong enough not to need stakes when the plant is used for forcing. As it rarely grows taller than 100 cm when mature, this shrub is ideal for mixed borders. If correctly grown in soil with a Ph of 5.5, the flowers are among the most luminous blues of all. The plant flowers mid-season, and there is sometimes a second show. Suitable for all regions. Illustration n° 12, page 27.

'BLÄULING' : Wädenswill, 1984. This cultivar is wrongly named 'Blauwtje' in Dutch and 'Teller Blue' in English. A plant in the "Teller" series, with dense inflorescences. The fertile flowers give the impression that a handful of very fine blue confetti has been thrown into the middle of the inflorescence, while the sterile florets, superimposed over them in two rows, have 3 or 4 slightly dentate sepals which are very short and wide. These are a beautiful mauvish blue, and are divided into two lobes rather like oxalis leaves. There are uneven changes in colour nuance as the season goes on, which make the final inflorescences very appealing indeed. The broad oval leaves are dark green, finely dentate and sharply acuminate. Growth is vigorous and dense. Flowering is prolific and takes place mid-season, sometimes with a second show of flowers. This is a shrub which is hardy and easy to grow, whether in tubs, in open beds or for forcing. In short, it is not far from being the ideal plant. Illustration n° 13, page 27.

'GENERALE VICOMTESSE DE VIBRAYE' : Emile Mouillère, 1909. This is a cross between *H. m. rosea* * and *H. m.* 'Otaksa', and is often mistaken for one or the other, as it combines the qualities of both its parents. Although darker than both parent plants, it is as beautiful with pink flowers as with blue, and does well in a wooded situation. The leaves are a rather pale green, and not very shiny. The "mop-head" inflorescences, which are normally 16 cm across, but can grow as wide as 20 cm, have strong stems, and are made up of sterile florets with 4 or, rarely, 3 entire sepals. These become tinged with crimson in autumn, and are very good for dried flower arrangements. In addition, flower buds also grow on the side branches, which guarantees that the plant will flower even when there are late frosts. It can grow up to 140 cm tall when mature. Suitable for all regions. Illustration n° 14, page 27.

'HAMBURG' : Schadendorff, 1931. A superb cultivar, still often seen today. It has rounded, more or less even inflorescences, up to about 20 cm wide, coloured deep blue in very acid soil, a mauve-tinged blue in more alkaline soil, and carmine pink in soil with a pH level of 6.5. The sterile florets are about 6 cm wide and usually have 3 very broad, very fimbriate wrinkled sepals, but there are some inflorescences where most of the florets have 5 sepals. In all cases, the sterile florets are closely packed together and all open at roughly the same time. The plant can be distinguished from 'Europa'* by the fact that its stems are green and not black. Its tough, shiny dark green foliage with rounded, sharply dentate leaves and its thickset habit give the plant a solid and resistant look, and rightly so. In addition, it is a good plant for use in forcing. Suitable for all regions. Illustration n° 16, page 28.

'KLUIS SENSATION' : Kluis, year unknown. This bush is spectacular when it flowers, for it appears to turn into one great mass of pale blue inflorescences. It is among the first cultivars to bloom : the fine colour of its flowers can be seen from the very first day of summer. The inflorescences are little round balls, roughly 14 cm across. Each branch produces an inflorescence, which explains why flowering is so prolific. The plant can be 130 cm tall before flowering, but the weight of the flowers bends the branches down to the ground and the plant loses half of its height. Unfortunately this early show of flowers does not last very long, and the inflorescences begin to fade from mid-July onwards. Suitable for all regions. Illustration n° 17, page 28.

'MARECHAL FOCH' : Emile Mouillère, 1924. This was for many years the cultivar that was most often grown for a fine blue colour, although its pink form is also pleasing. The "mop-head" inflorescences are produced on both terminal and lateral branches, ensuring that flowers will be produced even after the hardest winter. The sterile florets have four entire sepals which do not overlap when mature. A smallish plant with healthy foliage, for which a place can be found in any garden. Free-flowering. Suitable for all regions. Illustration n° 18, page 28.

'NIKKO BLUE' : A plant of unknown origin, but probably imported from a garden in the Nikko region of Japan. Although somewhat difficult to establish in the first two years after planting, it flowers most prolifically. The inflorescences are about 15 cm across, and are carried on tall, supple stems. The four sepals of the sterile florets are light and well-spaced, and always entire. Once established, the plant produces many new branches and dependable quantities of flowers, which are lavender blue. It is early-flowering, and thrives best in a slightly shaded position. Very easy to propagate. Mature height 140 cm. Suitable for sheltered regions. Illustration n° 19, page 28.

'OTAKSA' : Siebold. Imported from Japan in the 1860s. At the time of his first journey to Japan, Siebold had met a beautiful young girl, after whom he named this "mop-head" *Hydrangea macrophylla*. The spelling of 'Otaksa' is actually rather fanciful, as the girl's name was really Taki Kusumoto. In Japan at that time, people's first names were given the prefix "O", meaning "great" or "honourable", and the suffix "san", corresponding to "Mr", Mrs" or "Miss". Thus what von Siebold heard when the girl was first presented to him was "O - Taki - san", which became "O - tak - sa" on von Siebold's lips. This is a most elegant and majestic hydrangea, with broad hemispherical inflorescences about 23 cm wide, coloured a delicate blue. The plant can grow to over 2 metres tall when mature. The foliage is shiny, and very dark and healthy, with ovate leaves, except that the first two leaves underneath the inflorescence are typically obovate in shape. The sepals are entire, and not squashed up against one another. This is a finely delineated plant that is also very robust and prolifically flowering. It is the ancestor of all cultivars of *Hydrangea macrophylla* with thick woody stems. Suitable for all regions except those with a very severe climate. Illustration n° 15, page 27.

'RENATE STEINIGER' : August Steiniger, 1964. This plant produces the finest blue of all, close to the colour of forget-me-nots, when grown with this aim in view. "Mop-head" inflorescences are 15-17 cm across, fairly even in shape and size, and formed from star-shaped sterile florets 4 cm wide with 5 or 4 denticulate sepals which are mottled with white at the start of the flowering. In autumn the inflorescences turn a green-tinged crimson, with a few touches of soft blue. The elongated, clear green leaves have large, uneven teeth. In neutral soil, the colour turns to purple mixed with deep blue. Early flowering. Gives very good results both when grown in open beds and when used for forcing. The plant produces only moderate numbers of flowers but its overall performance is good. Mature height 140cm. Suitable for all regions. Illustration n° 20, page 29.

'UNIVERSAL' : Origin and year unknown. The exceptional regularity of this plant's inflorescences is striking. They are in the form of hemispheres all of the same diameter, i.e. 16 cm, formed from sterile florets with denticulate sepals. The colour is a splendid royal blue. This plant has irresistible appeal : impossible to ignore it in the middle of a collection. Its name is therefore well-deserved. Mature height is 120 cm, foliage mid-green, with rather small leaves. Dependable and prolific, with great resistance to pests and diseases. Suitable for all regions. Illustration n° 21, page 29.

PURPLE

'EISVOGEL' : Wädenswill, 1979. The name means "Kingfisher" and the cultivar is wrongly called 'Ijsvogel' in Dutch and 'Kingfisher' in English. This plant, whose inflorescences reach a width of about 15 cm, has sterile florets with 4 sepals that are quite characteristic : two of the sepals are placed opposite one another on one plane, while the other pair, similarly opposite one another, are on a different plane which crosses the first one at a 45° angle. These sepals are very broad, and acuminate. A large number of very small fertile flowers form a tightly-packed centre to the inflorescence. The overall colour is cobalt blue, fading towards the edges of the sepals of the sterile florets. Leaves are in the shape of attenuate ovals, but rather miserable-looking, being very susceptible to chlorosis and pest damage. It is therefore best to plant the shrub in combination with other plants, which will hide the foliage. Mature height is 120-140 cm. For regions with a mild climate. Illustration n°31, page 32.

'HOLSTEIN' : Schadendorff, 1928 or 1931. Named after the Holstein region of northern Germany. This plant is remarkable for the diameter of its sterile florets, which have denticulate sepals and can grow to a width of 8 cm, while the inflorescences themselves, which are salmon pink in neutral soil and purplish blue in acid soil, do not grow any wider than 14 cm. Leaves are small, elongated and only slightly dentate. The plant is late-flowering, and grows vigorously. It is a cultivar recommended for forcing, but also does very well in the open. Mature height around 140 cm. Suitable for all regions. Illustration n°25, page 31.

'JEANNE PENCHER' : Dublanchet, year unknown. A plant with purple "hortensia" inflorescences, uneven in shape, made up of broad sterile florets 6 cm in diameter. The sepals are almond-shaped, wide, entire, often wavy and with a beak-shaped tip. The foliage is bluish-green, with healthy, broadly dentate leaves. Although its colour is clear and crisp, this plant is not very original and the overall effect is rather uninspiring. Mature height is around 120 cm. Suitable for all regions. Illustration n°22, page 30.

'LA MARNE' : Mouillère, 1917. Certainly one of the finest French varieties, this shrub has everything to give pleasure. On top of the handsome shimmering dark green foliage grow inflorescences which are huge - up to 21 cm wide - and a quite unusual form and colour because of the very broad sterile florets of which they are composed. These are up to 6 cm wide and have 5 very sharply indented sepals, grouped together in a dish shape. The colour of each sepal is never exactly the same as the next one. The overall effect is of cream tones tinged with vibrant mauve, clear pink and pale green dotted with carmine, and darkening and turning more towards pinker tones with age. The woody stems are thick and well capable of supporting the flower heads. Flowering is most prolific, and begins in late July. Mature height up to 150 cm. Suitable for all regions. Indispensable. Illustration n°27, page 31.

'LANCELOT' : Wintergalen, 1920. A more slender relation of 'Parzifal', q.v.. The sterile florets which form the inflorescences have overlapping sepals of irregular width with fimbriate, wavy edges. The inflorescences are fairly uniform in shape - hemispheres 16 cm wide - and are blue or light mauve in acid soil (pH 5.5). A fine pink is obtained in neutral soil. Foliage is abundant and healthy, setting off the flowers well. Woody stems are thick and the plant is compact, not growing taller than 120 cm. A plant with a well-defined character, producing plenty of flowers and growing vigorously ; altogether commendable. Suitable for all regions. Illustration n°29, page 31.

'LAUSANNE' : Breeder and year unknown. A plant with "mop-heads" 15 cm wide, coloured a fine mid-purple in acid soil. Sterile florets have 4 entire sepals. Late flowering, sometimes with the flowers rather hidden by the leaves, which are clear green, of even size and shape, and not very shiny. A sturdy plant. Mature height up to 170 cm. Suitable for all regions. Illustration n°26, page 31.

'NACHTIGALL' : Wädenswill, 1979. The name means "Nightingale", and the plant is often wrongly called this in English-speaking countries, and 'Nachtegal' in Dutch. This shrub belonging to the "Teller" series has strikingly beautiful indigo blue inflorescences 15 cm wide which remind us of the fact that it is descended from *H. m.* 'Enziandom'*. The sterile florets are borne on long stalks and are arranged in a single row in the form of a coronet. They are formed from 4 - 5 entire sepals which are almost heart-shaped, slightly mottled with white in the middle and tinged with purple at the apex. The oval leaves are dark green, and not shiny. An upright shrub, not usually growing taller than 140 cm. There is sometimes a second flowering. Suitable for mild regions. Illustration n°32, page 32.

'PARZIFAL' : Wintergalen, 1922. A thick-set, solid, well-trained plant, rarely taller than 120 cm. Inflorescences are hemispherical, 16 cm wide, and their colour varies greatly according to the nature of the soil. It ranges from dark pink in neutral soil to deep blue in acid soil, but when the soil has a pH of around 6, the plant has the drawback of producing a range of rather nauseating intermediate colours. It is nevertheless a very good plant when grown in soil that is clearly acid or neutral. Sterile florets have 5 sepals that are deeply fimbriate and wavy at the tip, giving the plant an unforgettable appearance. A plant with a great deal of personality. Leaves are clear green, small, wrinkled and dentate. The inflorescences produce a distinct scent of privet in the sun. Suitable for all regions. Illustration n°28, page 31.

'PRESIDENT R. TOUCHARD' : E. Draps, 1938. A cultivar with loosely-packed "hortensia" inflorescences, more or less even in shape, about 18 cm wide. The sterile florets are a fine purple tinged with pink, with light green centres. The florets turn entirely to a purplish-pink in soil with a pH level of around 6.5. They have from 4 to 6 sepals ; these are oval in shape, either elongated or rounded, with fimbriate edges and mottled with white or pale mauve. Growth is rather slow but dependable, and the bush can reach a height of 130 cm when mature. Suitable for all regions. Illustration n°23, page 30.

'SOUVENIR DE MADAME EMILE CHAUTARD' : Emile Mouillère, 1909. Very often abbreviated to 'Mme Chautard'. A plant with very beautiful colouring : purplish-blue tinged with pink. Sterile florets have 4 sepals whose colour lightens towards the edges and which have a white spot at the tip. A hydrangea that irresistibly recalls the ones portrayed in old Japanese prints. Hemispherical inflorescences, 16 cm across. A very sturdy plant, growing to about 130 cm tall. It does not produce many flowers, but what wonderful flowers they are ! Suitable for all regions. Upright habit. Illustration n°24, page 30.

'TOVELIT' : Originally from Denmark, year unknown but apparently between 1950 and 1955. Sometimes called 'Tofelil'. An extraordinary little plant, very closely packed and not growing taller than 80 cm. The "mop-head" inflorescences are small (11 cm wide), frizzy-looking and very close together, packed against each other to form a single pink and mauve monochrome. Sterile florets have 4 or 5 pointed sepals, and leaves are narrow and tapering. Late flowering. Suitable for all regions. A delightful plant that is well worth getting to know. Illustration n°30, page 31.

1. **'Ave Maria'** *page 18*

2. **'Nymphe'** *page 18*

3. **'Regula'** *page 19*

4. 'Bachstelze' *page 18*

5. 'Elster' *page 18*

6. 'Sir Joseph Banks' *page 19*

7. 'Bichon'*page 18*

8. 'Louis Mouillère' *page 18*

9. 'Weisse Königin' *page 19*

10. 'Adria' *page 20*

11. 'Ardtornisch' *page 20*

12. 'Blauer Zwerg' *page 20*

13. 'Blaüling' *page 20*

14. 'Générale Vicomtesse de Vibraye' *page 20*

15. 'Otaksa' *page 21*

16. 'Hamburg' *page 20*

17. 'Kluis Sensation' *page 21*

18. 'Maréchal Foch' *page 21*

19. 'Nikko Blue' *page 21*

20. 'Renate Steiniger' *page 21*

21. 'Universal' *page 22*

22. **'Jeanne Pencher'** *page 23*

23. **'Président Touchard'** *page 24*

24. **'Souvenir de Madame Emile Chautard'** *page 24*

25. 'Holstein' *page 23*

26. 'Lausanne' *page 23*

27. 'La Marne' *page 23*

28. 'Parzifal' *page 24*

29. 'Lancelot' *page 23*

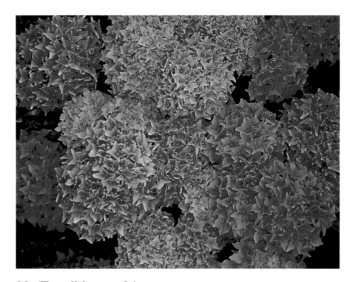

30. 'Tovelit' *page 24*

31. 'Eisvogel' *page 23*

32. 'Nachtigall' *page 23*

PALE PINK

'GOFFERSBERG' : Haller, 1978. Rather an ordinary-looking plant. Leaves are small, consistently oval, attenuate and dentate. Inflorescences are round, and about 14 cm wide. Sterile florets have 4 entire sepals, coloured a chalky mid-pink. The plant stands up nice and straight, and grows 120 cm tall. It is even-looking, and produces plenty of flowers. Suitable for all regions. Illustration n°34, page 41.

'MARIE-CLAIRE' : Dublanchet, year unknown (1964-67). This cultivar is a slightly chalky pale pink dotted with carmine, and has a rather sorrowful air about it. It does, however, produce very large quantities of flowers : big inflorescences that are loosely packed but regularly shaped. The 4 sepals making up the sterile florets are rounded and slightly dentate. Leaves are rounded, slightly acuminate and evenly dentate. The overall effect is somewhat lacking in surprise and sparkle. During its early years it can be rather a spindly plant, and is susceptible to chlorosis, so soil with a maximum pH of 6 is recommended, and plenty of feeding. Suitable for all regions except those with a particularly severe climate. Mature height around 170 cm. Illustration n°35, page 41.

'MARIESII' : Maries, 1879. Award of Merit. This plant was brought back to the Veitch Nurseries in England by the explorer Maries. It was the first hydrangea ever to be successfully propagated from seed, by the French plant-breeding genius Victor Lemoine. Most present-day cultivars possess "blood" from this hydrangea. It is a plant of a type midway between "hortensia" and "lacecap" whose inflorescences are very large, loosely-packed and graceful, and of a fresh pink colour. The shrub can grow to over two metres tall. The intense green leaves are very shiny and typically narrow, tapering and acuminate. A sturdy plant that grows vigorously. It produces its very beautiful flowers towards the middle of the season. Suitable for all regions. Illustration n°33, page 41.

'MÜCKE' : Wädenswill, 1968. This cultivar is wrongly called 'Mug' in Dutch, and 'Gnat' in English, which is a translation of its German name. A plant in the "Teller" series ; rather too stiff-looking. The inflorescences are white tinged with pink or mauve ; they have sterile florets neatly arranged around the outside, while the fertile flowers, relatively few in number and a deeper pink, decorate the centre. The sterile florets have absolutely round, slightly denticulate sepals, which go together to make a round flower. The leaves, too, are rounded, with one tooth sticking out at the tip. The wrinkled foliage is not, in fact, particularly good, and is susceptible to chlorosis. As the season progresses the inflorescences let themselves go a bit and their colour becomes more intense, giving the plant a less severe and more charming look. Mid-season flowering. Mature height not taller than 100 cm. An excellent plant for forcing, but should only be grown in the open in sheltered coastal gardens. Illustration n°37, page 42.

'PENSEE' : Unknown origin, before 1958. A good garden plant, little known. Inflorescences are about 15 cm wide, with broad sterile florets, pink edged, fading to white towards the centre, but turning completely pink when flowering reaches its peak. Sepals are almost entire or slightly scalloped. Foliage is tough, healthy and not very shiny. A plant rather lacking in originality. Mature height 130 cm. Suitable for all regions. Illustration n°36, page 42.

'POMPADOUR' : Jacques Neilz, 1962. A cross between 'Petite Soeur Thérèse de l'Enfant Jésus' * and 'Val du Loir' (q.v.). A very fine light pink, rather tending towards salmon. The plant is remarkable for the size of its inflorescences, which are up to 20 cm wide, and for its sepals, which are prettily serrated and sometimes mottled with green. The lacy inflorescences have an air of the 17th Century about them and the matt dark green foliage serves as a most appropriate background. The plant is widely used for forcing (it can even be seen in Japanese florists' shops) but will also do well in the open, although it is rather sensitive to cold.

Flowering is prolific and posture is upright. Good for arrangements of fresh flowers. Suitable for sheltered regions. Illustration n°38, page 42.

'SOUVENIR DE CLAIRE' : Of obscure origin, this plant is listed in Rovelli's catalogue in 1844. Is it a branch sport selected by Rovelli from among the plants he bought from Siebold, or even, as some authors have supposed, a plant grown from seed by Rovelli himself ? This does not seem likely. There is no mention of hydrangeas being grown from seed until much later, when Lemoine carried out his successful experiments, and in any case, as Rovelli was an Italian and lived in Italy, he would hardly have given a French name to one of his own plants. As all the hydrangeas stocked by Rovelli came from Siebold's nursery, it might be thought that the plant was named by Siebold himself, yet none of the Siebold nursery catalogues that have come down to us mention any plant called 'Souvenir de Claire'... Another theory holds that 'Souvenir de Claire' is a plant created in about 1909 in memory of the late-lamented little daughter of a lady friend of Emile Mouillère's. Obviously this cannot be the same as Rovelli's plant, which means that there must be two plants with the same name... The mystery remains unsolved. Be that as it may, the plant presented here is not lacking in interest. Inflorescences are a fine light pink, and a good size. Sterile florets are small and close together, generally made up of four broad, rounded and overlapping sepals, giving an overall effect that is gentle and easy on the eye. The plant also has the rare advantage of producing flowers on the current year's new branches. The flower heads grow on strong flexible stems which can reach a height of 180 cm. Resistant to disease, and readily turning sky blue in appropriate soil. The plant flowers prolifically and is extremely hardy. Suitable for dried flower arrangements. Well worth rediscovering. Illustration n°39, page 42.

DEEP PINK

'ATLANTICA' : Unknown origin and year ; before 1958. A hydrangea with a rather melancholy look, with inflorescences about 14 cm wide in the form of tufted domes, which recall the cultivar 'Floralia' (q.v.), although without the same imposing presence, for the stems are weaker and the colouring rather muddy. Sterile florets are very uneven in shape : the sepals are planted any old how, sometimes narrow and entire, sometimes broad and slightly denticulate, and there can be any number between 3 and 7. The light green leaves can sometimes be bifid, and are susceptible to chlorosis. In short, rather an odd plant, which does not flower until August and grows no taller than 130 cm. Suitable for all regions. Illustration n°42, page 43.

'CHAPERON ROUGE' : Louis Mouillère, 1954. Louis Mouillère was Emile Mouillère's son, and he too was bitten by the hydrangea "bug". His breeding experiments were directed towards obtaining the darkest colours possible, the "Holy Grail" being a perfect red. 'Chaperon Rouge' (French for "Red Riding Hood") was a decisive step on the way to this goal. Inflorescences are small, but present in large numbers. They are made up of evenly-shaped, flat sterile florets, whose sepals are more or less heart-shaped. Suitable for all regions. Illustration n°46, page 43.

'CONSTELLATION' : Although unknown, the breeder of this plant deserves to be proud to have created it. The light sterile florets, which are a beautiful clear pink, look like a circle of butterflies around the outside of the inflorescence. The sepals are sharply dentate and they overlap, with the ends of the "wings" touching. The form of the inflorescence is globular but irregular, and the effect is joyful. The blue-green foliage is of a similar high standard, serving as a perfect backdrop to set off the flowers. Suitable for all regions. Height 140 cm. Upright habit. Illustration n°43, page 43.

'DÜSSELDORF' : Unknown origin. A good plant, with small round inflorescences, 16 cm wide, overloaded with sterile florets pressed up against one another. The 3-4 sepals are extremely broad and short, entire or indented here and there, and coloured a very luminous deep pink. The deep green leaves are even in size and shape, oval, slightly acuminate, moderately dentate, tough and wrinkled. Autumn colours are remarkable : inflorescences take on a lovely old-rose colour, tinged with green. Maximum height 150 cm. Suitable for all regions. Illustration n°47, page 43.

'FIANCAILLES' : Unknown origin. The name, which means "Betrothal" in French, is often distorted to 'Franchailles' in English-speaking countries. This plant has unevenly shaped inflorescences that are altogether charming. The sterile florets are curious for their limp appearance ; they are made up of an irregular number of sepals which are loose, very broad and wavy when mature, but very narrow when their growth has been inhibited. The overall effect is reminiscent of a jumble of pale pink rags and is very pleasant indeed. Leaves and branches are stiff and very regular, making a striking contrast with the inflorescences. Not a prolifically flowering plant, but its general appearance is quite astounding. Height 130 cm. Suitable for all regions. Illustration n°40, page 42.

'FLORALIA' : Gijseling, before 1958. An exceptionally majestic plant with large "mop-head" inflorescences 18 cm wide growing straight upwards. These inflorescences are a pure mid-pink, and look like late 18th Century periwigs. The sterile florets have 4 sepals with pale undersides and a very curious shape, as though they were folded into a point ; this is what gives the inflorescence the look of a wig. Flowers are produced very early, with no second flowering. The shrub grows no taller than 130 cm. Suitable for all regions except those with a risk of late frosts. Illustration n°44, page 43.

'HORBEN' : Haller, 1973. Named after a Swiss mountain. The pale mauvish-pink inflorescences are more or less rounded, up to 16 cm across, and somewhat unevenly shaped. They are made up of small sterile florets with 4 sepals that are not dentate. Foliage is mid-green, healthy and abundant ; the rounded leaves have a very characteristic spoon shape, opening out towards the base. Mid-season flowering. The plant does not grow any taller than 100 cm. Suitable for all regions. Illustration n°45, page 43.

'MADAME G.F. DE BIER' : Draps-Dom, 1938. This little plant has inflorescences of a rather chalky dark pink colour ; their appearance is uneven, sometimes cleft or fissured. The small florets have 5-7 entire sepals, either elongated or widened. The small, faded green leaves do not look very attractive. This is a free-flowering plant growing no taller than 100 cm. Suitable for all regions. Illustration n°48, page 44.

'MARQUISE' : Cayeux, before 1964. This hydrangea has "hortensia" type inflorescences, 16 cm across. Their uniform colouring is rather boring, but their form, on the other hand, shows a certain originality ; a light and airy appearance, as there are very sparse numbers of sterile florets. These florets have 4 clearly separated sepals which are entire, rounded and slightly acuminate, and they grow on very long stalks which droop late in the season ; this, added to the fact that the sepals turn pale, gives the plant a melancholy look. Height 140 cm. Upright habit. Suitable for all regions. Illustration n°49, page 44.

'MERVEILLE' : Cayeux, 1927. This was one of the most important cultivars to be bred during the inter-war years. This was, in fact, the first time that the most important basic essentials were united in one plant : strong stems, intense colouring, abundant very large flowers and beautiful foliage. The plant was enormously successful right from the start, particularly as it is admirably suitable for forcing. Its big, evenly shaped, vivid pink "mop-heads", made up of large sterile florets, are still widely appreciated now. The 3 or 4 sepals are sharply denticulate, and their colours fade to beautiful tones of muted mauve. Mature height around 120 cm. Suitable for all regions except those with a very severe climate. Illustration n°50, page 44.

'MONTFORT PERLE' : Brugger, 1946. This plant's colour is rather a drab red but the ball-shaped inflorescences are very firm and exceptionally even in form and size. Sterile florets are 5 cm wide with 4 or 5 oval entire sepals which overlap a little. Growth is rapid but mature height does not exceed 110 cm. Mid-green foliage is rather fragile and susceptible to chlorosis. Upright, rigid habit. Needs a rich subsoil and a maximum pH of 5.8. Suitable for all regions. Illustration n°51, page 44.

'RIGI' : Unknown origin. A cultivar with really huge inflorescences, often more than 20 cm across, with broad, sharply denticulate sepals. Colour is rather a salmon pink. The stems are not always able to support the weight of the enormous flower heads. The mid-green leaves are large and wrinkled. In short, a splendid monster. Mature height around 120 cm. Suitable for sheltered coastal regions. Illustration n°52, page 44.

'ROSA ZWERG' : Unknown origin. The name means "Pink dwarf". A splendid-looking plant, whose ample, firm "mop-head" inflorescences are bright pink, around 16 cm wide, with straight stems. Their sterile florets have 4 round entire sepals. Leaves are healthy and of even size and shape. A bush which does not grow taller than 100 cm when mature. Suitable for all regions. Illustration n°53, page 44.

'STRATFORD' : Unknown origin. A shrub with rather loose-textured inflorescences about 14 cm wide, coloured a somewhat run-of-the-mill pink. The sepals of the sterile florets are entire and irregularly-shaped, with well defined veins. Foliage is wrinkled, lightish green, healthy and perhaps a bit too abundant as it tends to partially conceal the inflorescences. Mature height no taller than 110 cm. Suitable for all regions. Illustration n°54, page 45.

'TAUBE' : Wädenswil, 1979. The name means "Pigeon", and this cultivar is wrongly called 'Duif' in Dutch and 'Pigeon' in English. A cultivar in the "Teller" series. Inflorescences are 17 cm wide, and made up of large, languid-looking sterile florets coloured a slightly chalky mid-pink, arranged in a single row, overlapping around the outside of the inflorescence. The centre contains sparse numbers of fertile flowers the same colour as the sterile florets. The matt dark green leaves are oblong, with a slightly wavy surface. This shrub reaches a height of 160 cm when mature. For sheltered regions. Illustration n°41, page 42.

'TEGERFELDEN' : Haller, 1971. Named after a castle in Switzerland. A shrub whose flowers are outstandingly charming ; one might even say amazing, for the "mop-head" inflorescences, 17-20 cm wide, are made up of sterile florets with 4 or 5 entire rounded sepals which fit into each other, giving the florets the shape of a dish. The florets are a beautiful light pink, and have the additional advantage of only taking on this colour one after the other, which gives a very fresh look to the inflorescence.

The healthy, dark green foliage is very abundant, although without ever hiding the inflorescences. Mature height 120 cm. Free-flowering and sturdy, this shrub will do well in all regions. Illustration n°59, page 45.

'URSULA' : A plant of unknown origin, which recalls the 1930s. Each inflorescence looks like a bunch of African violets, coloured a fine bright pink. The inflorescences are made up of sterile florets whose sepals are wavy and sometimes, though rarely, denticulate, and which curl together and overlap to form a dish shape. Clear green foliage. Inflorescences take on very interesting autumn colours : greyish pink tinged with green and speckled with crimson. The shrub grows to 160 cm when mature. Suitable for all regions. Illustration n°56, page 45.

'VAL DU LOIR' : Unknown origin. A plant with inflorescences in the form of soft, flattened spheres, up to 16 cm wide, coloured a rather chalky mid-pink. The sterile florets are quite extraordinary, as they take on the bilobate outline of oxalis leaves. They have entire edges, but are extremely wavy. All this gives very squashy-looking flowers, which are at their peak from late July to early August. This is a robust plant, growing to a maximum height of 110 cm. Suitable for all regions. Illustration n°55, page 45.

'VORSTER FRÜHROT' : Steiniger, 1951. This plant has inflorescences 15 cm wide that are most curious, being made up of a profusion of sterile florets that become coloured at different rates, giving the inflorescences the look of two-tone balls coloured soft green and very dark pink. The leaves are very acuminate and edged with carmine. A sturdy, problem-free plant that grows to a mature height of 140 cm. Suitable for all regions. Illustration n°57, page 45.

'YVONNE CAYEUX' : Cayeux, 1920. A shrub with classic large, perfectly regular inflorescences and fine healthy rounded leaves. The inflorescences only have an original appearance at the beginning of flowering, as the sterile florets of which they are made do not "ripen" at the same rate, giving an odd mixture of clear pink and green. A plant that produces dependable quantities of flowers, without any nasty surprises. Height 150 cm. Suitable for all regions. Illustration n°58, page 45.

RED

'AARBURG' : Haller 1973. Named after a castle in the canton of Aargau in Switzerland. A plant that has regular "hortensia" inflorescences with a light, airy appearance, about 23 cm wide, made up of unusually wide sterile florets (5-7 cm across) on long stalks, with clearly separated cherry-red sepals that are oval and entire. Although the plant is very free-flowering, some of the inflorescences can often be concealed under the abundant foliage. The light green leaves are oblong or oval, acuminate and sharply dentate. Mid-season flowering. Mature height up to 120 cm. Susceptible to chlorosis. Suitable for all regions. Illustration n°60, page 46.

'BRUGG' : Haller, 1971. Synonym 'Cristel'. A hydrangea with dark pink inflorescences that are rounded but uneven in shape, with fertile flowers in the form of a quadrilateral with pointed tips. The sterile florets have 4 rhomboid entire sepals, with large and small ones together on the same floret. Leaves are rounded, dentate and acuminate. Their shiny dark green colour gives them a very healthy appearance. Can be used for forcing. Very early flowering. Habit can sometimes be lacking in erectness, as the stems are thin. Mature height 90 cm. Suitable for all regions. Illustration n°61, page 46.

'ELMAR STEINIGER' : Steiniger, 1956. A cultivar with inflorescences of a really fabulous red ; they are in the form of spheres about 15 cm across, and when they are seen against the deep green foliage, the overall effect is most impressive. Unfortunately this shrub is susceptible to pest damage and should therefore be closely watched. Sterile florets have 4 fimbriate sepals. The very wrinkled, tough leaves have broad teeth around their edges and very well-defined veins. Woody stems are thick, and the habit is upright. Not very free-flowering. Height 120 cm. Suitable for all regions. Illustration n°62, page 46.

'EUGEN HAHN' : Steiniger, 1980. A densely-growing plant with characteristic mid-bluish-green foliage. The leaves are very wrinkled, denticulate and slightly acuminate, and are crowded together very closely on thick stems which contribute towards the ornamental character of the plant. The bright reddish-pink inflorescences are fairly small but grow in very large numbers, following one another throughout the season. The plant is early flowering and has very appealing autumn colours : a mixture of carmine and greyish pink. Pointed, slightly denticulate sepals. Sterile florets closely packed together. Does not always perform well when used for forcing. Mature height around 100 cm. Suitable for all regions. Illustration n°63, page 46.

'GIMPEL' : Wädenswil, 1987. A cultivar in the "Teller" series, wrongly called 'Bloedvink' in Dutch and 'Bullfinch' in English. Although inflorescences are essentially of the "lacecap" type, they often have sterile florets growing from the centre. The florets are a pure dark pink, and have 4 sepals which overlap in a very attractive way. Sepals are completely rounded, very wide, with slightly scalloped edges. Fertile flowers are the same colour, but open to reveal a white interior. The mid-green shiny leaves are heart-shaped, acuminate, with broad teeth round the edge. A shrub with plenty of character, not growing taller than 120 cm. Mid-season flowering. Suitable for sheltered regions. Illustration n°64, page 46.

'HARLEQUIN' : Steiniger, 1957. Originally named 'Sensation 75', but as the name 'Sensation' had already been given to another plant before 1957, the nickname 'Harlequin' is the one that should now be officially used. An exception among hydrangeas ; the broad, denticulate sepals are red with white borders, and give an unusual and joyful look to the plant. A vigorously growing plant ; the stems, although thin, are sturdy. Inflorescences have an untidy appearance, and late flowers can be of a single colour. An amusing shrub, which should be used with restraint. Not very hardy. Maximum height near to 100 cm. Illustration n°72, page 48.

'HARRY'S RED' : Unknown origin. A medium-sized plant with hemispherical inflorescences whose crimson colour is exceptional. Their shape is uneven, and there are also uneven numbers of sepals. These are entire, and tend to be rolled up towards the centres of the sterile florets. The florets do not all open at the same time, and the green colour of the immature ones avoids what might otherwise be a monotonous appearance. Foliage is sparse and frail. Suitable for all regions. Illustration n°65, page 46.

'KARDINAL' : Wädenswill, 1989. A Swiss cultivar in the "Teller" series. A sturdy shrub, with very abundant, healthy foliage and inflorescences which have deep red sterile florets in a single or double row. These have four entire sepals which are very elongated and curve inwards, and are rather like a less accentuated version of those of H.m. 'Rotschwanz', (q.v.). The fertile flowers open up in the centre of the inflorescence, in a range of tones from mid-pink to mauve. The attractive dark green leaves are wrinkled, markedly denticulate, rounded and attenuate. Habit is dense and upright, and growth is vigorous. Mature height 140 cm. Mid-season flowering, sometimes with a second show of flowers. Suitable for sheltered gardens only. Illustration n°66, page 47.

'LEUCHTFEUER' : Dienemann, 1962. The name means "Beacon Light". synonym 'Herman Dienemann'. A plant with inflorescences 14 cm wide, coloured a dark, slightly chalky red, remarkably dense and even, in the shape of flattened spheres, produced in relatively small numbers. Flat sterile florets with 4 sepals. Leaves are broad, very acuminate, oblong and matt, with brown edges. A vigorous, upright, early-flowering plant. Mature height rarely greater than 100 cm. Sensitive to late frosts. suitable for all except particularly severe regions. Illustration n°67, page 47.

'LIEBEGG' : Haller, 1970. A cultivar with inflorescences of the "hortensia" type, in the form of light, airy hemispheres about 15 cm across, coloured a beautiful deep pink. The sterile florets, with 4 entire or slightly scalloped sepals in the form of elongated ovals, have a tousled appearance which gives plenty of charm to the plant. Leaves are oval, moderately dentate and slightly wrinkled. Does not seem to grow taller than 100 cm. Should be planted in a rich subsoil, in a mixed border or in a pot. Suitable for all regions. Illustration n°68, page 47.

'MADAME AIME GIJSELING' : Gijseling, between 1954 and 1964. The name is sometimes strangely distorted to 'Ude Amegyselink' by Dutch nurseries ; it deserves greater consideration than this, for it is a superb plant. The rather small inflorescences are made up of very broad sterile florets with 5,6,7 or even 8 strongly fimbriate sepals coloured a fine reddish-pink, tinged with white or light pink. The shrub is vigorous but does, however, have the drawback of being susceptible to chlorosis. The sharply dentate leaves are not very attractive and are best concealed by the foliage of other plants. Maximum height around 140 cm. Suitable for all regions. Illustration n°69, page 47.

'MAMAN' : Dublanchet, year unknown. In spite of its rather insipid name, this is one of the most beautiful red hydrangeas of the "hortensia" type. The colouring is uniform but not monotonous, because of its unique velvety texture. Inflorescences are about 16 cm across, made up of very soft sterile florets which look like little silk squares. The four sepals are even in size, with entire, wavy edges. The bluish-green leaves are elongated, tapering and finely dentate, and tend to partially conceal the flowers. A vigorous plant, widely used for forcing. Suitable for all regions. Maximum height 180 cm. Illustration n°70, page 47.

'MERKUR' : Brugger, year unknown. One of the finest of the mid- to late-flowering varieties of red "hortensia" type hydrangeas. Star-shaped sterile florets with 4-5 wide, acuminate sepals which have a characteristic central stripe and are occasionally mottled with a lighter colour. Rather light, unevenly shaped hemispherical inflorescences about 14 cm wide. Oval mid-green leaves. The plant is of upright habit, with a second flowering, and is recommended for use in forcing. Mature height rarely greater than 100 cm. Suitable for sheltered regions. Illustration n°71, page 47.

'ROTDROSSEL' : Wädenswil, 1987. A cultivar that is wrongly called 'Koperwiek' in Dutch and 'Redwing' in English. It is a plant in the "Teller" series with broad, glowing crimson red inflorescences. The sterile florets are very large, forming a multiple coronet around the outside of the inflorescence, and have 4 overlapping, elongated, slightly dentate sepals which curve inwards. The centre of the inflorescence contains mauve fertile flowers with white stamens, giving the impression that they are frosting over. Leaves are slightly shiny, sharply dentate and coloured a fine dark green. This is one of the "Teller" plants that is most resistant to cold conditions. Illustration n°73, page 48.

'ROTSCHWANZ' : Wädenswil, 1987. the name means "Redstart", and this cultivar is sometimes wrongly called 'Roodstaart' in Dutch and 'Redstart' in English. A superb plant from every point of view ; one of the greatest successes in the "Teller" series. The sterile florets have 4 entire, elongated sepals with a groove down the middle, giving the floret the shape of a blood-red cross, which is typical of this cultivar and quite unforgettable. Inflorescences are flat, about 18 cm wide, with fertile flowers at the centre which, when they open, look like a circle of white and red embroidery. Autumn colours are astonishing ; the inflorescence takes on a deep dark-red wine colour. The foliage is dark green, wrinkled and healthy. The plant flowers towards the middle of the season, and its mature height is around 120 cm. Suitable for all but the most severe regions. Illustration n°75, page 48.

'SATINETTE' : Lemoine, 1916. A fine plant with lovely reddish-pink rounded inflorescences, 14 cm wide, growing on pliable branches. Sterile florets have 3-5 broad, entire, acuminate sepals which are rather soft in texture. The dark foliage is exceptionally healthy, with abundant, wrinkled, dentate leaves, and the colours of the foliage and the flowers harmonize exceptionally well together. Mature height 160 cm. Very free-flowering. Suitable for all regions. Illustration n°74, page 48.

'SONTAGSKIND' : Steiniger, 1979. The name means "Sunday's child", who is, of course, "fair and wise and good and gay", but who is also, according to the Germans, "born lucky". A cultivar with a very fine dark red colour. The round inflorescences, 17 cm wide, grow well above the foliage. The mid-green, shiny leaves are very wrinkled, sharply dentate and acuminate, and they set off the flowers to advantage. The dish-shaped sterile florets are even in size and shape, having four sepals with broadly scalloped edges, slightly elongated but not acuminate. Mature height no greater than 120 cm. Suitable for all regions. Illustration n°77, page 48.

'TICINO' : A pretty dwarf plant of unknown origin, whose inflorescences - evenly-shaped "mop-heads" up to 20 cm across - are a fine dark pink colour. The sterile florets have four broad, rounded or heart-shaped sepals whose colour is enlivened by white centres and sometimes by whitish mottling. Leaves are light green, wrinkled and not very shiny. The abundant foliage sets off the inflorescences, which turn to a beautiful greyish pink late in the season. A very vigorous, free-flowering plant, up to 100 cm tall. Suitable for all regions. Illustration n°76, page 48.

33. 'Mariesii' *page 33*

34. 'Goffersberg' *page 33*

35. 'Marie Claire' *page 33*

36. 'Pensée' *page 33*

37. 'Mücke' *page 33*

38. 'Pompadour' *page 33*

39. 'Souvenir de Claire' *page 34*

40. 'Fiançailles' *page 35*

41. 'Taube' *page 36*

42. 'Atlantica' *page 35*

43. 'Constellation' *page 35*

44. 'Floralia' *page 35*

45. 'Horben' *page 35*

46. 'Chaperon Rouge' *page 35*

47. 'Düsseldorf' *page 35*

48. 'Mme G.F. De Bier' *page 35*

49. 'Marquise' *page 36*

50. 'Merveille' *page 36*

51. 'Montfort Perle' *page 36*

52. 'Rigi' *page 36*

53. 'Rosa Zwerg' *page 36*

54. 'Stratford' *page 36*

55. 'Val du Loir' *page 37*

56. 'Ursula' *page 37*

57. 'Vorster Frührot' *page 37*

58. 'Yvonne Cayeux' *page 37*

59. 'Tegerfelden' *page 36*

60. 'Aarburg' *page 38*

61. 'Brugg' *page 38*

62. 'Elmar Steiniger' *page 38*

63. 'Eugen Hahn' *page 38*

64. 'Gimpel' *page 38*

65. 'Harry's Red' *page 38*

66. 'Kardinal' *page 39*

67. 'Leuchtfeuer' *page 39*

68. 'Liebegg' *page 39*

69. 'Mme Aimé Gijseling' *page 39*

70. 'Maman' *page 39*

71. 'Merkur' *page 39*

72. 'Harlequin' *page 38*

73. 'Rotdrossel' *page 39*

74. 'Satinette' *page 40*

75. 'Rotschwanz' *page 40*

76. 'Ticino' *page 40*

77. 'Sontagskind' *page 40*

CHAPTER 3

OTHER HYDRANGEA SPECIES

Collector's plants

Natural plants

COLLECTOR'S PLANTS

H. aspera 'Mauvette' : A plant of obscure origin, but undoubtedly English, and known for many years in the horticultural literature. It is smaller and stiffer than *H. aspera villosa*, and has hemispherical inflorescences 15 cm across, with plenty of fertile flowers in the centre and sterile florets around the edge, both types of flowers being coloured an unforgettable pure mauve. Foliage is not very abundant, and unremarkable. Flowering takes place from early to late July, thus being rather too short-lived, although worthy of admiration, particularly as the faded inflorescences take on an elegant greyish-pink colour which lasts until early September. Should be planted in a position sheltered from cold winds. Illustration n° 78, page 57.

H. aspera 'Peter Chappell' : A plant of obscure origin, named by Maurice Foster in honour of a great English plantsman (see Volume 1). This cultivar, like all *H. aspera*, has downy leaves ; these are 15 cm long and 7 cm wide, and also have downy stalks. The branches, too, are downy. Both the fertile flowers and the sterile florets are white. The inflorescences are of the "lacecap" type, and grow up to about 20 cm wide ; they open in August. The shrub grows to a height of 150 cm, and a similar width, when mature. It is a rare and splendid variety of this species. Illustration n° 79, page 57.

H. heteromalla 'Aréthuse' : Corinne Mallet, 1992. Named after Arethusa, the nymph who was changed into a fountain. This plant was bred from a seedling grown by Lady Ann Palmer from seeds collected on the frontier between Nepal and Tibet by Tony Schilling during the 1980s. It is a thick-stemmed plant with a weeping habit, which is rare and exceptional for the genus *Hydrangea*. Flowering is very abundant, and takes place in June. The creamy white inflorescences are of the "lacecap" type and are about 15 cm across ; they grow on curved branches and appear at different levels, giving a majestic air to the plant. Foliage is rather sparse, with oval, denticulate leaves 16 cm long and 5 cm wide. This plant is at the moment the only one that exists (is is being propagated) and does not yet seem to have reached its full mature height ; it is at present 150 cm tall. Illustration n° 98, page 60.

H. heteromalla 'Edouard d'Avdeew' : Robert Mallet, 1992. A cultivar bred from an unnamed seedling grown by Edouard d'Avdeew a few years before his death, and now named in memory of him. Although this plant has the general features typical of *H. heteromalla*, its slender growth and the extreme abundance of its inflorescences make it particularly remarkable. These inflorescences are 17 cm across, and are a lovely creamy white when they open, turning to a bright reddish pink as they fade. Flowering takes place in June, but the faded flowers remain attractive for a further month. Like all *H. heteromalla*, this plant can grow very big, and should therefore be allowed plenty of space when it is planted. Illustration n° 99, page 60.

H. paniculata 'Bridal Veil' : Jelena and Robert De Belder, 1990. One of the most extraordinary *H. paniculata* varieties. A supple plant, with thin, hanging branches. Inflorescences are small but remarkable, having sterile florets up to 4 cm across whose sepals are very broad and sharply cut out ; quite an extraordinary feature for this species. The inflorescences are produced in succession throughout the season ; it is possible to use them in dried flower arrangements, although they are rather fragile. The plant is a selection made from a seedling of *H. paniculata* 'White Moth' *. Flowering takes place from early August until the first frosts. Illustration n° 82, page 58.

H. paniculata 'Brussels Lace' : Jelena and Robert De Belder, 1975. The plant was bred from a seedling of 'Unique'*. A dense, ball-shaped, branchy shrub. The paniculate inflorescences open in late July. They are composed of a cushion of large numbers of yellowish-beige fertile flowers on which are scattered the off-white sterile florets, which are very small. The overall effect is of openwork lace, hence the name. It does not grow taller than 200 cm, and is thus a less cumbersome size than *H. paniculata* 'Unique'. Foliage is healthy. The sterile florets become unevenly spotted with pink at the end of the season. It produces abundant, dependable flowers, from early August until the first frosts. Illustration n° 83, page 58.

H. paniculata 'Greenspire' : Jelena and Robert De Belder, 1975. A fine, well-spaced looking bush, with very light paniculate inflorescences of a greenish-white colour growing well clear of the foliage on shoots 30 cm long and 20 cm wide, made up of sterile and fertile flowers, with many leaves growing mixed in with the flowers. Growth is rapid and flowering is dependable, but it should be planted in partial shade to protect the flowers from excessive bright sunlight.

The inflorescences turn a definite green towards the end of the flowering season. In arrangements of fresh flowers they are of real value for setting off pink and red colours to advantage. This is another plant bred from a seedling of *H. paniculata* 'Unique'*. Flowering from late July to late September. Illustration n° 84, page 58.

H. paniculata 'Kyushu' : A plant from the island of Kyushu in Japan, brought to Europe by Collingwood Ingram early this century, but distributed by Robert and Jelena De Belder who had received the explorer's cuttings which were labelled *"Hydrangea paniculata,* medium form, from Kyushu". The two main attractions of this plant are its upright habit, and the fact that it produces extremely abundant flowers right from its early years. The paniculate flower heads are made up of many fertile flowers and wide sterile florets which are a fine white. The plant is greatly appreciated for its natural look. A sturdy plant, with healthy foliage. Late flowering, from late August to the first frosts. Illustration n° 85, page 58.

H. paniculata 'Melody' : Jelena and Robert De Belder, 1985. A majestic plant, with a soaring flight of inflorescences on thrusting, slender branches. The inflorescences are exceptionally long - over 35 cm - compared with a width of about 18 cm - and the plant itself can grow to 4 metres tall. The panicles are "S"-shaped, very delicate and light, with sparse numbers of sterile florets, starting very early in the season and continuously opening to give a beautiful off-white colour, tending towards pure white. They can be used in dried flower arrangements. This elegant plant was bred from a seedling of *H. paniculata* 'Unique'*. It flowers from mid-July to late September. Illustration n° 86, page 58.

H. paniculata 'Mount Everest' : Hillier, probably around 1989. A plant which flowers latish in the season, from mid-August to the first frosts. This sturdy shrub has large, luxuriant paniculate inflorescences, made up of pale pink fertile flowers and sterile florets which begin creamy-white, turning pale pink late in the season. Award of Merit, 1990. Can grow taller than 300 cm. Illustration n°87, page 58.

H. paniculata 'Papillon' : Jelena and Robert De Belder, 1985. A plant bred from a seedling of *H. paniculata* 'Unique'*, growing up to 300 cm tall. The inflorescences, which grow on strong branches, are both long and wide, and are produced in large numbers in August. They have a profusion of sterile florets with raised sepals, giving the impression of a cloud of white butterflies. A very graceful plant. Flowering from late August to the first frosts. Illustration n° 88, page 59.

H. paniculata 'Pink Wave' : Edouard d'Avdeew, around 1980. A shrub having very long branches with sparse numbers of leaves, on which grow panicles which are about 20 cm long and 20 cm wide, with many greenish-white fertile flowers on which are scattered dish-shaped sterile florets up to 4 cm wide. These are pure white at first, quickly turning to greenish white then, late in the season, to pink, at which time the fertile flowers also change colour, to a reddish pink. Mature height around 250 cm. A very free-flowering plant, producing flowers from late July to late September. Illustration n° 89, page 59.

H. paniculata 'Ruby' : Jelena and Robert De Belder, 1990. This shrub, bred from a seedling of *H. paniculata* 'Pink Diamond'*, has inflorescences with abundant sterile florets. It flowers early, and takes on a carmine pink tint from August onwards ; this colour deepens gradually, becoming dark pink at the end of the season. It is a very good plant for dried flower arrangements, although some people find the late season colour almost too intense. Grown commercially in the USA (Monrovia Nursery, Oregon), but it should be appearing on the European market soon. It flowers from late July until the first frosts. Illustration n° 90, page 59.

H. paniculata 'Tardiva' : Unknown origin - possibly Hillier. Year unknown. One of the latest flowering varieties, with rather small paniculate inflorescences which only have sterile florets on the lower parts. The plant is very similar to *H. paniculata* 'Kyushu', q.v., and is only slightly later flowering that the latter. It flowers from mid-September until the first frosts. Illustration n° 91, page 59.

H. paniculata 'Vera' : A shrub with light and airy forms. As the plant's origin is unknown, we do not know whether 'Vera' really is the name of a horticultural cultivar or whether the breeder simply wished to say that it conforms to the species type (*vera* = true, in Latin). The light green foliage acts as a good background for large numbers of small paniculate inflorescences, whose sterile florets have very long stalks ; an extremely characteristic feature. Flowering takes place from early August to late September, with the drawback of not producing any interesting late season colours. Illustration n° 92, page 59.

H. quercifolia 'Harmony' : Thomas Arthur McDaniel, year unknown. A supple-stemmed bush, with a tendency to sink under the weight of its inflorescences ; it therefore needs to be staked when young. The leaves are about 15 cm long, deeply lobed, like those of all *H. quercifolia* plants, and they take on lovely colours in autumn. The paniculate inflorescences are irregularly shaped, and made up mostly of slightly off-white sterile florets, pressed closely together to give an overall appearance rather like an enormous, vaguely pear-shaped snowball, 30 cm long by 20 cm wide. Mature height over 250 cm. Flowering from mid-July to late September. Illustration n° 94, page 60.

H. quercifolia 'Sikes Dwarf' : Louisiana Nursery, year unknown. A shrub that is very close to the wild form of *Hydrangea quercifolia*, but smaller. The paniculate inflorescences are creamy white, regularly shaped, up to 30 cm long by 15 cm wide. They have a thick cushion of pinkish-beige fertile flowers, on which are scattered very pale yellow sterile florets with entire, non-wavy sepals. The leaves have long stalks. Its habit is firmer than most other *H. quercifolia* cultivars. The shrub does not grow taller than 150 cm. It flowers from early August to late September. A good plant for arrangements of fresh flowers. Illustration n° 95, page 60.

H. quercifolia 'Snow Queen' : Bill Flemer, year unknown. A plant with a good, firm habit, the branches having no tendency to sink under the weight of the flowers. The paniculate inflorescences are made up of very large numbers of greenish-white fertile flowers, and of large numbers of broad sterile florets, divided into four lobes, slightly wavy, with a colour that is only just off-white and which quickly becomes tinged with pink. The sterile florets are about 3 cm across. This is one of the earliest flowering varieties of *H. quercifolia* ; flowering starts in mid-July and goes on until mid-September. The shrub can grow up to 250 cm tall. Illustration n° 96, page 60.

H. quercifolia 'Tennessee Clone' : Jelena and Daniel De Belder, 1974. A plant selected from seed collected in Tennessee. It is remarkable for the great abundance of its broad sterile florets, which have 4-5 very wavy sepals, white with the slightest hint of pale green, but turning to green at the end of the season. The paniculate inflorescences are 25 cm long and 20 cm wide, and have a rather tousled look with plenty of style ; they look feminine and assertive at the same time, and make one think of Scarlett O'Hara ! The leaves are also quite remarkable, being very deeply lobed and very wrinkled. The shrub has plenty of character and can grow to a height of 200 cm, even though its prostrate habit when immature means that it needs to be staked when young. It flowers from early August to late September. Illustration n° 97, page 60.

H. serrata 'Tiara' : Maurice Foster, 1990. A plant selected for a number of features which make it exceptional. The inflorescences have an abundance of both fertile and sterile flowers, and are of a type halfway between "hortensia" and "lacecap" ; they are a fine blue colour when they open, turning mauvish pink and then finishing dark pink. The foliage is dark crimson when exposed to sunlight all day, and takes on a flaming crimson colour in autumn. The flowers themselves remain attractive until the first frosts This is a very free-flowering plant with a most healthy appearance. It flowers from mid-June to mid-July, with the flowers remaining attractive until mid-August. Mature height is not greater than one metre. It should be planted in partial shade. Illustration n° 93, page 59.

H. serrata 'Ramis Pictis' : This cultivar is normally considered to belong to the species *macrophylla*, but is really much closer to the *H. serrata* species. It was introduced from Japan in the 1890s, and has often been considered synonymous with *H. macrophylla* 'Nigra'* ; it is, however, quite a different plant. *H. m.* 'Nigra' is a slender cultivar with spindly stems which are such a dark purple colour that they look black. Its inflorescences are ball-shaped and pale pink or pale blue, and its leaves are pale green. *H.m.*'Ramis Pictis' is, on the other hand, a squat plant with thick stems and pinkish-white inflorescences of the "lacecap" type with sparse numbers of sterile florets which have 4 entire sepals. Its leaves are dark green, with red veins and stalks. The stems are fairly light in tone ; their colouring is in tones of carmine, but this colour is superimposed like a mottled veil over a background colour of very light green. This surface colour of carmine looks rather as though a light stocking had been drawn on over a pale leg. The effect is indeed one of "painted stems" It may be that because of the resemblance between "pictus", meaning "painted" or "coloured", and "picus", meaning "black", writers became confused between *H.m.* 'Ramis Pictis' and *H.m.* 'Nigra'. Maximum height 150 cm. Suitable for all regions. Flowering from late June to late July. Illustration n° 80, page 57.

H. serrata subsp. yezoensis 'Wryneck' : Named after a type of European woodpecker. A plant which is wrongly considered in the West as being a member of the species *macrophylla*, but whose features clearly indicate that it belongs to the *serrata* species. Only its inflorescences, in the shape of irregular spheres, remind one of the *macrophylla* species, but these lack the well-defined structure of *H. macrophylla* inflorescences[1]. In Japan, this plant's common name is Ezo-ajisai, which makes it synonymous with *Hydrangea serrata* subsp. *yezoensis*[2], and observation confirms that it does indeed belong to this sub-species. Apart from the ball-shaped form of the inflorescences, an accident which can occur in almost all hydrangea species, there is only one feature that would indicate the possibility of cross-breeding with a different sub-species of *serrata* : the fact that the very pale leaves, unlike those of *H. serrata* subsp. *yezoensis*, are not rich in anthocyans. Japanese specialists nevertheless consider it to be a completely separate *H. serrata* subsp. *yezoensis*, as the plant is found in exactly this form growing in the wild, far from the natural habitat of other *serrata* sub-species. It is known by the name of 'Temari-ezo-ajisai' in Japan or else it is given the name 'Niwa-ajisai'.

It is known that this plant was brought from Japan, but we know neither when it was imported, nor by whom[3]. The inflorescences have a tendency to "bow their heads" in a typical way. The intense blue of the inflorescences and the fact that it is very early flowering make it a remarkable garden plant. Flowering is, nevertheless, over by the end of July, as with other varieties of *serrata*. Very free-flowering. Does not seem to grow any taller than about 120 cm. An excellent plant for dried flower arrangements early in the season. Illustration n° 81, page 57.

1 See Appendix, p. 101
2 See the entry in the second part of this chapter
3 "The Hydrangeas", by Michael Haworth-Booth.

NATURAL PLANTS

H. aspera D.Don **var. macrophylla** Hemsley : An exceptionally majestic plant, as broad as it is tall, reaching a maximum height of nearly 300 cm. The dark bluish-green leaves are oval and serrulate, with thick down on both surfaces. Their total length is 30 cm, including the stalk, which is 4 cm long, and they are 15 cm wide. The branches, leaf stalks and main veins are reddish, and they too are covered in thick down. Inflorescences are of the "lacecap" type, 25 cm wide, and they open at the beginning of July. They grow on branches which lean out slightly so as to hold them away from the main body of the bush, rather like trays being held at arm's length. The abundant fertile flowers which make up the greatest part of the inflorescence are dark purple, while the sterile florets are pure white, and form a coronet around the outside. The flowers fade at the end of July. The plant is native to China. Illustration n° 114, page 64.

H. strigosa (Rehder) : This plant is close to *Hydrangea aspera* subsp. *aspera,* and can be distinguished from the latter firstly by the nature of the down on the leaves. The hairs on the underside are short and straight, and grow flattened against the surface. A few scattered hairs covering the capsules can be observed in certain plants. In addition, while a reddish or purple tint can be observed in the branches, stalks and leaf veins of many other *H.aspera, Hydrangea strigosa* never shows the slightest trace of this ; all of these parts are always pale green. Another striking feature is the flowering period ; other types of *aspera* never flower before mid-July, whereas *H. strigosa* has already finished flowering by this time. Inflorescences are of the "lacecap" type, up to 15 cm across. Sterile florets are sparse, and coloured pale pink ; the fertile flowers are a deep, luminous purple. the leaves are elongated and lanceolate, with rounded attenuate tips, the limb being up to about 24 cm long by 9 cm wide, and the stalk about 10 cm long, giving a total length of about 34 cm. The plant seems able to grow up to three metres tall in the wild. A batch of specimens of this plant was once distributed in England with the name *H. longipes,* but the latter can be clearly distinguished from *H. strigosa* because its leaves are oval and the hairs are not flattened. *H. strigosa* is native to China. Illustration n° 113, page 64.

H. hirta (Thunberg) Siebold and Zuccarini : This plant is known as the "Nettle-leafed hydrangea" in the West, but so few westerners had seen it that one hardly dared to believe in its existence. It is a native of Japan, growing on well-lit, wooded volcanic slopes from 600 metres upwards. It is highly probable that the photograph of the plant in this book is the first to be published in the West. It is a strange, very graceful plant, with leaves from 3 to 10 cm long and 2.5 to 7 cm wide, the length being up to two and a half times greater than the width. The leaves are oval and sharply dentate, with serrations from 3 to 8 mm deep, and they do bear a certain resemblance to nettle leaves. They are dark green. Woody parts are spindly, and the stems are tinged with crimson or mauve. Inflorescences are small but numerous, from 2 to 10 cm wide. Their colour is from creamy white to pinkish white, and there is a complete absence of sterile florets. The plant can grow up to 150 cm tall when mature. The photograph is of a specimen growing in the wild. Illustration n° 101, page 61.

H. integrifolia Hayata : A native of Formosa (Taiwan) and the Philippines. This plant belongs to the *Monosegia* subsection of the *Cornidia* section, and is the only member of the *Cornidia* section that is native to Asia. It resembles *H. Seemannii** in most respects, but it has larger inflorescences and smaller sterile florets. Inflorescences are white and about 20 cm across ; they are made up of fertile flowers, with sterile florets dotted among them. The shrub has a creeping or climbing habit, and has aerial roots growing from its branches. The dark green leaves are evergreen, thick, very slightly or not at all dentate, oval, and about 30 cm long by 5 cm wide. The branches are covered with coarse reddish hairs. The plant does not normally produce its first flowers until it is about fifteen years old. Illustration n° 115, page 64.

H. involucrata Siebold **'Viridescens'** : A plant discovered growing wild on the island of Yakushima in Japan. It has all the usual features of *H. involucrata** but has one astonishing characteristic : the sterile florets of its inflorescences are pale green and not white or mauve. These green florets make a superb contrast with the violet fertile flowers. This is a very free-flowering shrub, and the overall effect is one of great character. It is a little later flowering than other types of *H. involucrata*. Illustration n° 102, page 61.

H. paniculata Siebold : A many-branched tree or shrub, growing up to 700 cm tall. Leaves are opposite or, more rarely, ternate, oval, smooth on the upper surface but with hairs along the veins underneath. They are up to 20 cm long by 10 cm wide. The paniculate inflorescences are made up of fertile and sterile flowers which are always white, tinged with greenish yellow or very pale pink. They can grow to a length of more than 30 cm. Many variations of this plant exist both in wild and in gardens. It needs to be planted in a sunny position in order to flower properly. Native to Japan. The photograph is of a specimen growing in the wild. Illustrations n° 100, page 61 et n° 103, page 62.

H. paniculata Siebold **f.velutina** (Nakai) Kitamura : A form introduced to Europe by James Russell. It is a plant that has most of its features in common with *H. paniculata*, but it can be distinguished from the latter by its prostrate habit, its small inflorescences and leaves, and above all by the feltlike covering of downy hairs on its leaves, stalks, branches and inflorescences ; the inflorescences do not come into bloom before mid-August or early September, but stay decorative until the first frosts. Illustration n° 104, page 62.

H. paniculata Siebold **'Mont Aso'** : Jelena and Robert De Belder, 1970. This plant was collected at the summit of the volcano Aso on the island of Kyushu in Japan ; it was found growing in a place where one might have expected the volcanic smoke, gases and ash to prevent the growth of plants. This plant is very late flowering, and can grow to a great width in a suitable environment. It is even later flowering than the cultivar 'Tardiva', (q.v.). Illustration n° 105, page 62.

H. scandens (L.f.) Seringe : Native to Japan and Formosa (Taiwan). A shrub about 150 cm tall, with inflorescences made up of fertile and sterile flowers. The fertile flowers are in the middle of the inflorescence, with the sterile florets around the edge. The sterile florets are off-white or yellowish, few in number, with 3 or 4 sepals, the one furthest from the centre of the inflorescence being considerably broader than the others. Leaves are oval, 5 cm long by 2.5 cm wide, only slightly dentate and coloured a dull dark green. Rather difficult to grow. Illustration n° 108, page 63.

H. scandens (L.f.) Seringe **gr.angustipetala** : Native to Japan, Formosa (Taiwan) and China. This plant hardly grows taller than 150 cm, but is most spectacular, as much for its foliage as for its flowers. Inflorescences are white, with fertile flowers at the centre which have petals that are elongated and narrow, not triangular like those of other hydrangeas. The sterile florets around the edge of the inflorescence have four spatulate sepals whose edges are broadly dentate or, rarely, entire. The leaves are narrow, around 7 cm long by 2 cm wide, and are completely and deeply dentate in a characteristic way that is unique for the genus. It is for painstaking collectors only as, like all *H. scandens* plants, it is rather difficult to grow. Illustration n° 107, page 63.

H. serrata (Thunberg) Makino **'Hallasan'** : This hydrangea is native to the Hallasan National Park in South Korea, on the island of Cheju (otherwise known as Quelpart). It is a dwarf bush, not growing taller than 80 cm, but extending horizontally in a curious way as it produces runners or stoloniferous branches, taking over more and more ground in this way ; this dense growth means that it could very well be grown as a ground cover plant. Leaves are oval acuminate and sharply dentate, 16 cm long by 7.5 cm wide, coloured a lovely dark green very rich in anthocyans, which gives broad crimson marks to the foliage. The leaves have very short stalks, about 1 cm long. Inflorescences are of the "lacecap" type, coloured from pink to light mauve, with fertile and sterile flowers that are altogether curious, for the number of petals varies from 3 to 8, the number of stamens from 8 to 14 and the number of styles from 2 to 8. It is possible that the strange construction of this plant is the result of an inherited genetic accident [1]. Illustration n° 109, page 63.

H. serrata (Thunberg) Makino **'Tenuifolia'** : A miniature plant in every respect. It forms a bush no more than 80 cm tall, with extremely thin stems that have trouble standing up straight during the plant's early years. Foliage is reddish, with minutely serrated leaves growing to a maximum size of 9 cm long by 2.5 cm wide. Inflorescences are from 2 to 6 cm wide (!) and are of variable form, sometimes being made up just of fertile flowers, and

---

[1] See the section on mutations in the Appendix.

sometimes being a mixture of fertile and sterile flowers. Both sorts of flower beat all records for smallness. The number of the different parts of the flowers is extremely variable. It is quite likely that this plant is completely sterile. It is a clone that seems typical of the kind of mutation that results from overexposure of the seeds to the sun.[1] Illustration n° 110, page 63.

H. serrata (Thunberg) Makino **subsp. angustata** Sugimoto : A hydrangea that is typical of the slopes of Mount Fuji, where it is found in large numbers ; it does, however, also grow on all the other mountains along the east coast of the island of Honshu in Japan, from Mt. Hayachine in the north to Mt. Ibuki in the south, from an altitude of 600 m upwards. It is a bush that never grows more than 100 cm tall. It can easily be recognized by its leaves, which are light green, very narrow and with whitish stalks and veins. The branches are long, thin and sinuous, and inflorescences grow one after the other along at least two thirds of their length. The smooth bark is mahogany brown. The inflorescences are of the "lacecap" type, rather small - about 7 cm across - and are composed of both fertile and sterile flowers. Both types of flower are completely white, including the petals, stamens, and styles of the fertile flowers, a feature which makes the plant quite exceptional for the *Macrophyllae* sub-section. The sterile florets normally have four sepals. Observation of the natural habitat of this plant has demonstrated that only four types of hydrangea are found in this habitat : *H. involucrata*, *H. paniculata*, *H. hirta* and *H. serrata* subsp. *angustata*. All the different parts of this plant have characteristics and colouring that are particular to itself, and which are never found in other representatives of the *H. serrata* species. In addition, other *H. serrata* are never found in the natural habit of *H. serrata* subsp. *angustata*, and the features of *H. serrata* subsp. *angustata* are constant throughout its natural habitat. All this leads one to think that the plant is not just a variety, but a real sub-species. The photograph shows a specimen growing in the wild. Illustration n° 111, page 63.

H. serrata (Thunberg) Makino **subsp. yezoensis** (Koidzumi) Kitamura : A well-distinguished sub-species, growing in northern Japan, in the southern half of the island of Hokkaido (formerly Ezo) and on the island of Honshu from the extreme north as far as Mt. Hayachine on the east coast and Mt. Shiruma on the west coast. A plant with an upright habit and straight branches on which grow oval or oblong dark green leaves, spotted with broad crimson areas on the parts exposed to the sun. The leaves have characteristic sharply dentate edges and long, acuminate tips. The limbs of the leaves are wrinkled and have scattered hairs ; the stalks and veins are reddish and covered with a thin layer of dense, whitish feltlike down. Flowering takes place between mid-June and mid-July. The plant has cymiferous inflorescences of the "lacecap" type, but the different ramifications within them are very elongated and less clearly defined than those of the "lacecap" type of *H. macrophylla*, and they terminate in a varied, random way. Sparse numbers of very small fertile flowers grow in the middle. The pink or blue sterile florets are well-developed, measuring 3-4 cm across ; They can be either entire or dentate depending on the individual plant, and grow in a coronet surrounding the fertile flowers. The bush itself is dense with many branches ; it has plenty of character, and remains interesting even after flowering has finished. Illustration n° 112, page 63.

H. serratifolia (Hooker & Arnott) Philippi f. : Native to Chile. A plant in the *Polysegia* sub-section of the *Cornidia* section. This sub-section comprises plants with inflorescences that grow in distinct bunches, one behind the other, and which have no sterile florets. The inflorescences of *H. serratifolia* are spectacular, for their extremely long stamens give them a downy appearance. They grow to a width of about 15 cm, sometimes more, and are off-white in colour. The leaves present a form of dimorphism which is particularly striking in this species : the older leaves are dark green, tough, shaped like elongated ovals and with slightly dentate edges, whereas the young leaves are mid- to light green, egg-shaped, truncated or rounded at the base, with entire edges, and are remarkably supple. Both old and young leaves are hairless. Like all plants in the *Cornidia* section, this shrub has a creeping or climbing habit. Illustration n° 116, page 64.

H. sikokiana Maximowicz : A bush between 1 and 2 metres tall, whose branches, inflorescences and stalks are pubescent. The leaves are lobate, with from 4 to 6 lobes, roughly 20 cm long by 12 cm wide, and with pubescent veins. The leaf stalks are remarkably long. The white inflorescences are of the "lacecap" type and are about 20 cm across, with a central mass of fertile flowers forming the greater part, and with sterile florets scattered over the surface. This is the only Asian hydrangea to have lobed leaves. Native to Japan. Illustration n° 106, page 62.

---

1 See the section on mutations in the Appendix.

78. H. aspera 'Mauvette' *page 50*

79. H. aspera 'Peter Chappell' *page 50*

80. H. serrata 'Ramis Pictis' *page 52*

81. H. serrata ssp. yezoensis 'Wryneck' *page 53*

82. H. paniculata 'Bridal Veil' *page 50*

83. H. paniculata 'Brussels Lace' *page 50*

84. H. paniculata 'Greenspire' *page 50*

85. H. paniculata 'Kyushu' *page 51*

86. H. paniculata 'Melody' *page 51*

87. H. paniculata 'Mount Everest' *page 51*

88. H. paniculata 'Papillon' *page 51*

89. H. paniculata 'Pink Wave' *page 51*

90. H. paniculata 'Ruby' *page 51*

91. H. paniculata 'Tardiva' *page 51*

92. H. paniculata 'Vera' *page 51*

93. H. serrata 'Tiara' *page 52*

94. H. quercifolia 'Harmony' *page 52*

95. H. quercifolia 'Sikes Dwarf' *page 52*

96. H. quercifolia 'Snow Queen' *page 52*

97. H. quercifolia 'Tennessee Clone' *page 52*

98. H. heteromalla 'Aréthuse' *page 50*

99. H. heteromalla 'Edouard d'Avdeew' *page 50*

100. H. paniculata près du Mont Fuji *page 55*

101. Hydrangea hirta *page 54*

102. H. involucrata 'Viridescens' *page 54*

103. H. paniculata *page 55*

104. H. paniculata f. velutina *page 55*

105. H. paniculata 'Mont Aso' *page 55*

106. H. sikokiana *page 56*

107. H. scandens gr. angustipetala *page 55*

108. H. scandens *page 55*

109. H. serrata 'Hallasan' *page 55*

110. H. serrata 'Tenuifolia' *page 55*

111. H. serrata ssp. angustata *page 56*

112. H. serrata ssp. yezoensis *page 56*

113. H. strigosa *page 54*

114. H. aspera var. macrophylla *page 54*

115. H. integrifolia *page 54*

116. H. serratifolia *page 56*

CHAPTER 4

THE CULTIVARS OF JAPAN

Hydrangeas in Japan
by Takeomi Yamamoto

Japanese Cultivars

HYDRANGEAS IN JAPAN
by Takeomi Yamamoto.

Japan is the paradise of hydrangeas, with more than ten species, distributed over the whole country. In addition, like many other plants, they all have their own separate habitats.

For example, *H. serrata* subsp. *yezoensis* is found in a region with heavy snowfall, in northern Honshu and Hokkaido, whereas *H. involucrata* lives in the central region of Honshu. (Japan consists of four main islands ; these are, starting from the north : Hokkaido, Honshu, Shikoku and Kyushu).

H. serrata grows in the inland mountainous area of central and eastern Honshu.

The natural habitat of *H. macrophylla* is the 'Izu Neven Islands' and the coastal area of the Kanto district on the Pacific coast of central Honshu. *H. macrophylla* is, above all, the endemic species of Japan, and it has major characteristics : vigour, large flowers and glossy leaves.

It seems that our ancestors gave the name 'Ajisai' to *H. macrophylla* plants with the "hortensia" type of flowers, but that this name gradually came to be applied to all plants belonging to the *Macrophyllae* sub-section in Japan. The name can be found in the 'Manyoshu', which is the oldest anthology of Japanese poetry, written in the 8th century. The name also features in instructions for 'Ikebana', the traditional Japanese art of arranging cut flowers, which dates from the 15th century.

During the Edo era (1603 - 1868), the cultivation of 'Ajisai' became very popular, and some cultivars such as *H. serrata* 'Beni-Gaku' and *H. serrata* 'Shichidanka' were displayed in the tea room to welcome guests to the Japanese tea ceremony. When Japanese people celebrated the birthday of the Buddha in Buddhist temples on 8th April every year, they would drink 'Amacha', which is a sweet-tasting infusion made from leaves of special clones of *H. serrata*. This commemorated the Chinese tradition that sweet-tasting rain fell on the day that the Buddha was born.

The name 'Ajisai' can also be found in 'haiku' written during the Edo period. 'Haiku' is a fixed verse form of 17 syllables, arranged in a five-seven-five pattern.

In these ways, the Japanese adopted 'Ajisai' as part of their way of life, their literature and their religion. I do not think that any country other than Japan has ever taken the hydrangea into its culture in such a profound way.

'Ajisai', which had only been admired by the Japanese, were finally introduced to Europe by von Siebold's book "Flora Japonica", at the end of the Edo era. Following this, by the early 20th century, Western horticulturalists had used some Japanese varieties to breed a large number of garden varieties of hydrangea.

On the other hand, the Japanese seemed to lose interest in collecting and hybridizing these plants during the period up to World War II. After the war, however, many people started to become interested in them, and began investigating wild species in order to collect plants with beautiful colours or rare shapes.

There are now about 150 different Japanese cultivars which have been selected from wild species. Apart from this, there are also many modern garden varieties, bred by both European and Japanese breeders. Thus we can take pleasure both in the simple flowers of plants selected from natural species and in the graceful flowers obtained by many different hybridizers.

Since von Siebold's time, nobody has carried out research into Japanese hydrangeas in the way that he did. Until today, there has been no exchange between Japan and Europe of precise information about Japanese hydrangeas. However, Corinne Mallet, the author of this book, has visited Japan three times and carried out serious investigations into the subject.

I hope that her work will lead to the introduction of Japanese hydrangeas all over the world, and that European horticulturalists will be able to adapt modern Japanese cultivars to European growing conditions.

Tokyo, 20 September 1994.

Takeomi YAMAMOTO

Takeomi Yamamoto is the greatest Japanese expert on hydrangea cultivars. He is the author of several monographs on the genus, and is now in charge of the biggest collection of Japanese hydrangea cultivars in the world. He corresponded with the late Michael Haworth-Booth, the famous British hydrangea collector, and he continues working for the promotion of better knowledge of Japanese hydrangeas.

JAPANESE CULTIVARS

H. macrophylla 'Domotoi' : This plant's name comes from a certain Mr Domoto, a Japanese who lived in the United States. In Japan, it is called 'Setsuka-Yae'. It flowers later than most other *H. macrophylla*, grows to a height of 200 cm, and has a rather spindly-looking outline. The plant is a mutant which has been grown in Japan for a very long time. The sterile florets are double or very double, either with several florets "stacked" on top of each other on the same stalk, or with abonormally large numbers of sepals and petals. This *H. macrophylla* also has the particular feature of sometimes having leaves which are ternate rather than opposite. The photograph[1] was taken at Tenryu in Japan. Illustration n°117, page 73.

H. macrophylla 'Hanabi' : This plant was named by Mr Takeomi Yamamoto who discovered it in 1960 or thereabouts. The name means "Firework" in Japanese. A many-branched and free-flowering plant which grows to an exceptionally large size : up to 250 cm tall. The "lacecap" inflorescences are broad, with a diameter of up to 20 cm, and have very double sterile florets with narrow, elongated sepals. Their colour is white, tinged with mauve or pink, and they continue to bloom until the autumn. This is one of the most dazzling Japanese cultivars. Illustration n°120, page 74.

H. macrophylla 'Izu-no-Hana' : This plant was discovered by Hisashi Iida around 1970 in the Izu peninsula. The name means "Flower of Izu".[2] The inflorescences are of the "lacecap" type, with large numbers of closely-packed fertile flowers in the centre and sterile florets on very long stalks evenly spaced around the outside of the inflorescence without touching one another. These sterile florets have a triple or quadruple row of very narrow, elongated entire sepals of different sizes, with the smallest ones nearest to the centre. The whole inflorescence is a splendid deep purple in acid soil and a fine pink in neutral soil. It is one of the most beautiful Japanese cultivars. Illustration n°119, page 73.

1. All the photographs in this chapter were taken in Japan.
2. Izu is a peninsula on the east coast of Honshu in Japan.

H. macrophylla 'Midori Uzu' : this is in some ways the green version of 'Ayesha'* Like 'Ayesha', which is called 'Uzu' in Japan, its sepals are spoon-shaped and thick in texture. The inflorescences of 'Midori Uzu' are, however, smaller than those of 'Ayesha', and, as we see, are coloured dark green. It is possible that this is due to a virus, and it is therefore inadvisable to grow this plant until such time as the reason for its unusual colour has been found. Illustration n°124, page 75.

H. macrophylla 'Shiro Gaku' : This plant is a Japanese selection with the rare characteristic of having entirely white fertile flowers. In fact the "lacecap" inflorescences are completely white throughout. The sterile florets have from 3 to 5 rounded entire sepals. For enlightened collectors only. Illustration n°122, page 74.

H. serrata 'Amagi-amacha' : A plant discovered around 1925 by Dr Makino in the Shizuoka prefecture. As the leaves are sweet-tasting, in Japan it is grouped together with the cultivar *H. s.* var. Oamacha, but nevertheless differs considerably from the latter both in its flowers and its foliage. The "lacecap" inflorescences have rather broad, white sterile florets with entire sepals in the shape of elongated ovals. Its leaves and branches are reminiscent of *Hydrangea serrata* subsp. *angustata*. It is a very free-flowering plant and the flowers are shown off to advantage by the foliage. It does not grow more than 100 cm tall. Illustration n°126, page 75.

H. serrata 'Beni-gaku' : Known for a very long time in Europe, having perhaps been introduced by Philipp Franz von Siebold. It is a selection made in Japan at an early date, and can be seen portrayed in old Japanese paintings and prints. An extremely graceful plant which has disappeared from the European commercial market ; an absence which ought to be rectified. Maximum height 1 metre ; moderately free-flowering ; "lacecap" inflorescences. The sepals of the sterile florets are white, becoming tinged with red. White fertile flowers. Illustration n°129, page 76.

H. serrata 'Hakucho' : The inflorescences of this hydrangea consist of sterile florets, generally four in number, pure white, very double, made up of egg-shaped sepals "stacked" on top of each other in order of size. The fertile flowers are sparse. Leaves are narrow and light in colour. Extremely graceful. Does not grow very large. Illustration n°118, page 73.

H. serrata 'Iyo Gasuri' : A cultivar whose "lacecap" inflorescences have purple fertile flowers with long stamens terminating in white anthers, and sparse numbers of sterile florets which have 4 pink sepals, tinged with mauve and clearly mottled with white. Such clear mottling is rarely seen in hydrangeas, and gives an unusual appeal to this plant. Illustration n°134, page 78.

H. serrata 'Kiyosumi' : A plant discovered by Mr Yasaka Hayasha in around 1950 on Mount Kiyosumi in the Chiba prefecture. The "lacecap" inflorescences have sterile florets with 4 rounded sepals which are white with red edges (the opposite of *H.m.* 'Harlequin'). The leaves are acuminate with sharply serrated edges. Fertile flowers are pinkish-white. A small plant. Illustration n°127, page 76.

H. serrata 'Kurenai' : A shrub whose supple stems and healthy foliage show off the inflorescences to advantage. These are of the "lacecap" type, with pinkish fertile flowers in the centre and sterile florets around the outside, whose white sepals gradually turn red, starting from the tip. When the red colour has reached half way along the sepals, the appearance of the inflorescences is strongly reminiscent of a watercolour drawing. Illustrations n°125, page 75 et n°132, page 77.

H. serrata 'Kurenai Nishiki' : A hydrangea which is very closely related to the cultivar 'Kurenai', with similar entire sepals, usually 3 to each sterile floret. The white surface of these sepals becomes progressively covered with red, starting at the tip and gradually spreading towards the base during the flowering period. Leaves are green, variegated with pale yellow. Should be used with restraint. Illustration n°139, page 80.

H. serrata 'Kurohime' : This plant is native to Nara and has been distributed and made known by the great Japanese collector Mr Takeomi Yamamoto, who is the author of several books on the genus. It is a small plant with inflorescences coloured a fine, dependable purple. Handsome light green foliage and black-tipped branches help to show off the inflorescences, which are small (not more than 10 cm wide) but present in large numbers. The sterile florets are single, and the fertile flowers are rather large, with beautiful stamens that have deep purple filaments. The mature plant is astoundingly lovely to look at. Illustration n°121, page 74.

H. serrata 'Maiko' : A small, many-branched, free-flowering shrub. Inflorescences are spherical but loosely-packed, made up of mauve sterile florets, generally with 4 sepals, and of darker fertile flowers. The fact that both sterile and fertile flowers are clearly visible contributes greatly to the appeal of the inflorescences. Leaves are slender and elongated, mid-green with lighter coloured veins, and lead one to think that this plant could be a hybrid of *H. serrata* subsp. *angustata*. Illustration n°133, page 78.

H. serrata 'Midori' : A plant discovered by Mr Takiko Fujita in 1988 in Shizuoka prefecture. The name means "Green". This Japanese selection has spherical inflorescences with sterile florets that stay completely green from the beginning to the end of the flowering season. This absence of colouring could be due to a viral infection. As the virus could be transmitted to other hydrangeas, it is considered inadvisable to grow this cultivar. These green-flowered plants seem in any case to be extremely delicate and likely to die sooner or later. Illustration n°123, page 75.

H. serrata 'Miyama-yae-Murasaki' : A cultivar with very well-structured "lacecap" inflorescences of a dependable violet colour. The name means "Miyama double mauve", Miyama being the district of Kyoto where the plant was discovered by Mr Takeshi Seto in around 1950. The fertile flowers are small, and the scattered sterile florets are very double with egg-shaped sepals arranged in order of size, the smallest being nearest the middle of the inflorescence. A spectacular and majestic plant. Illustration n°128, page 76.

H. serrata 'Niji' : The name means "Rainbow". A cultivar with "lacecap" inflorescences. The mauve fertile flowers are not particularly remarkable, but the sterile florets, on the other hand, are most unusual. They have 3 or 4 rhomboid sepals which are coloured cobalt blue at the base and gradually change in tone to become a bright purplish-pink at the tip. This extraordinary colouring explains and justifies the name of this elegant and free-flowering cultivar. The abundant handsome green foliage sets off the inflorescences to advantage. Illustration n°136, page 79.

H. serrata 'Oniji" : The name means "Large rainbow". This cultivar bears a great resemblance to 'Niji' in the colour of its sterile florets, but the colouring is less intense and the sepals are bigger and more rounded. Less spectacular than 'Niji'. Illustration n°137, page 79.

H. serrata 'Shichidanka Nishiki' : A cultivar which is closely related to *H. serrata* 'Stellata'. The difference lies firstly in the colour of the inflorescences, which are darker than those of 'Stellata', and secondly in the fact that it has variegated leaves. In fact this shrub's foliage is variegated with pale yellow to the extent that an entire half of some leaves is completely yellow. A very small plant. Illustration n°138, page 79.

H. serrata 'Shiro Maiko' : A completely white version of the cultivar 'Maiko', but the fertile flowers are less noticeable than those of 'Maiko' owing to the fact that they are the same white as the sterile florets. The inflorescences are smaller than those of 'Maiko'. Illustration n°141, page 80.

H. serrata 'Shirotae' : A small, very graceful plant. The name means "Bleached cotton", and it was discovered by Mr Shogo Okamoto in 1950 or thereabouts. It has rather small inflorescences made up of sparse white fertile flowers and a few quite wonderful sterile florets. These too are white ; they are very double and even in form, made up of a stack of sepals in descending order of size, and pointed like Gothic arches. Foliage is dark, with narrow leaves. One of the most marvellous Japanese hydrangeas. Illustration n°140, page 80.

H. serrata 'Yae-no-Amacha' : A plant discovered by Shigeru Tada in Niigata in around 1960. The name means "Double sweet tea", and it is a variant of *H. serrata* var.Oamacha, the difference lying in the nature of its "lacecap" inflorescences. These have sterile florets which are double in a random, anarchic way, similar to those of 'Domotoi'. They are coloured a very delicate pinkish-white. The plant rarely grows taller than 1 metre. Illustration n°131, page 77.

H. serrata var. Oamacha (Honda) : Known in Japan from time immemorial, this plant does not look particularly remarkable, but it does have one astonishing characteristic : its leaves are sweet, and can be used to make a sweet and mellow-tasting infusion. The plant is not grown on an industrial scale in Japan in the way that tea is, but is cultivated in the gardens of private homes or Buddhist temples. It was described in one of the first books to be printed in Japan, for it has medicinal properties. It grows wild in forests and produces many naturally-occuring variants which are collected and grown for their ornamental value. It is a many-branched shrub not growing more than one metre tall, with matt leaves, 9 cm long and 4 cm wide, with reddish stalks. Inflorescences are of the "lacecap" type, with abundant light pink fertile flowers and clear pink sterile florets which are single, with rounded sepals, and are arranged in a single coronet around the outside of the inflorescence. The infusion from this plant is traditionally drunk to celebrate the annual festival of the Buddha. Illustration n°130, page 77.

117. H. macrophylla 'Domotoi' *page 69*

118. H. serrata 'Hakucho' *page 69*

119. H. macrophylla 'Izu-no-hana' *page 69*

120. H. macrophylla 'Hanabi' *page 69*

121. H. serrata 'Kurohime' *page 70*

122. H. macrophylla 'Shiro Gaku' *page 69*

123. H. serrata 'Midori' *page 70*

124. H. macrophylla 'Midori Uzu' *page 69*

125. H. serrata 'Kurenai' *page 70*

126. H. serrata 'Amagi-Amacha' *page 69*

127. H. serrata 'Kiyosumi' *page 70*

128. H. ser. 'Miyama-yae-Murasaki' *page 70*

129. H. serrata 'Beni-gaku' *page 69*

130. H. serrata var. Oamacha *page 71*

131. H. serrata 'Yae-no-Amacha' *page 71*

132. H. serrata 'Kurenai' *page 70*

133. H. serrata 'Maiko' *page 70*

134. H. serrata 'Iyo Gasuri' *page 70*

135. H. serrata 'Niji' *page 71*

136. H. serrata 'Niji' *page 71*

137. H. serrata 'Oniji' *page 71*

138. H. ser. 'Shichidanka Nishiki' *page 71*

139. H. serrata 'Kurenai Nishiki' *page 70*

140. H. serrata 'Shirotae' *page 71*

141. H. serrata 'Shiro Maiko' *page 71*

CHAPTER 5

CULTIVATION
and
DECORATION

CULTIVATION

Climate

Depending on which species they belong to, hydrangeas have growing positions they prefer. *H. macrophylla* are the ones which will best put up with a partially sunny position and poorly drained soil, whereas *H. serrata* and most other species require a shady position with light, humid soil. *Hydrangea paniculata* and *H. heteromalla* will tolerate very porous, rocky or sandy soils, even in full sunlight. It would not, however, be possible to grow hydrangeas in excessively dry conditions without there being some artificial supply of water.

A western coastal climate is by far the best for all hydrangea species. They can be planted facing in any direction. In northern and eastern Europe, it is better to plant them in a west-facing position, and to avoid such species as *H. sikokiana* and *H. aspera* altogether. In inland France south of the Loire and in a Mediterranean climate, a south-facing position should be avoided as far as possible, and soil humidity should be closely watched during summer. The harsh climate and soil of mountainous regions calls for the hardiest species : *H. paniculata* or *H. heteromalla*. It is always possible to try growing other species, as local microclimates will often allow for exceptions to the rule. It should, however, be noted that the climate in towns is always drier than in the countryside and more attention should therefore be paid to watering.

If the growing area can be arranged so that it is shaded from 11 am to 6 pm, when the light of the summer sun is at its strongest, and so that the soil is kept well watered, all species can easily be grown in most of Europe, apart from mountainous areas and where the general climate is too harsh.

Soil

A good garden loam of the sort one might find in a vegetable garden, neither too heavy nor too light, is best for growing all species. The lightness of very sandy soils should be corrected by adding clay, and they should be well-fed as they are always poor in nutrients. This type of soil should be dug over a whole bed at a time, if possible the winter preceding planting. If more time is available for preparation, it should be enriched by digging in well-rotted manure and left for at least a year before planting.

Heavy soils can suffocate plants and should be lightened up by adding leaf mould in a proportion of about 50/50. The addition of coarse salt-free sand is also beneficial, as it will encourage root growth.

Rocky soils are the most difficult. They are very porous and need to be "stuck together" with clay to stop water draining away. Leaf mould should also be added, to give them the humus they lack. Proportions should be determined according to the partial or total absence of different nutrients in the soil. All these remedies should be applied bearing in mind that the ideal soil one is trying to create is good garden loam.

Feeding

In soils that are more or less well-balanced, fertilizer should be applied in dried form every other year in April or May. A fertilizer for plants that prefer acid soil, of the sort that is sold in bags, should be chosen. Two or three handfuls should be spread around the base of each plant, and watered in as soon as possible. It is important not to apply too much fertilizer at a time, and not to apply it too often, otherwise it will encourage foliage to grow instead of flowers. The best water is rain water. If you do not have access to this and your tap water is hard, soften it by adding a couple of tablespoonfuls of vinegar to each watering can. A pH level of 6.5 is best for hydrangeas with pink or white flowers. For blue flowers, a much more acid soil is recommended, down to a pH level of 5.

How to plant

If the plant is delivered without a pot or tub, the base is usually enveloped in a loose-woven sack which holds together the roots and the soil in which they have grown. All one needs to do is to cut the sack so as to free the roots before planting. If the plant is in a pot, it should be taken out and the mass of roots should be freed and spread out before planting. It sometimes happens that a plant has stayed in its pot too long and become pot-bound, with the roots coiled up into a dense "root ball". It should not be planted in this state, as the roots would not be able to get free by themselves and the plant would soon wither. The root ball should be split from top to bottom on four sides using a grafting knife or some other sharp cutting tool. The roots should then be disentangled by hand before planting.

The hole dug for planting needs to be double the width and depth of the roots. A little of the earth dug out should be pushed back into the hole to raise the plant so that the point where the stems join the roots is at exactly the same level as the surrounding soil. Before placing the plant in the hole, one or two handfuls of dried fertilizer should be sprinkled in, then covered with a thin layer of earth to avoid direct contact with the roots. Once the plant is in place, the hole should be filled in, then thoroughly watered so that the soaked soil fills in all the gaps between the roots. If this is not done, the air in these cavities will cause the roots to dry out. The fertilizer should be the kind sold for plants that prefer acid soil. The soil should be kept well watered at all times, particularly during the first month after planting. The pH level of the soil should be around 6, but it is better to err in the direction of acidity rather than alkalinity.

PROPAGATION

Cuttings

The taking of cuttings is the method most often used for propagating hydrangeas, as well as most other woody shrublike plants, as it requires the removal of only a small part of the plant and it can be completely relied on to reproduce the horticultural characteristics of the parent plant. What is more, it is very easy to take cuttings from hydrangeas, and a success rate of 90-100% is by no means unusual.

Branches or parts of branches that have not yet hardened are the ones that should be selected for cuttings ; they should be green, tender and full of water. Cuttings are normally taken in spring, around April or May, but can be taken at any time so long as there is no risk of freezing. The branches are divided into segments, each of which has two pairs of leaves or leaf buds. The lower pair of leaves is removed and the cuttings are stuck into pots or garden frames containing a mixture of one third garden soil, one third leaf mould and one third sand. The exact mixture and its proportions, can be varied according to personal experience and intuition. The cuttings should be two-thirds buried, leaving just the top pair of leaves and a short length of stem exposed. If the leaves are too well-developed they should be trimmed back to half their size with clean secateurs, to minimize loss of water through evaporation. The cuttings should then be watered copiously, preferably with rain water. Pots should be placed in the shade, and garden frames in a north-facing position.

It is essential to water the soil every day for a week, then more or less every second day during the second week, and so on... taking care that the soil is always kept humid. Be careful not to disturb the cuttings when watering. In a greenhouse, roots will have developed after ten days ; in the open this will take from one to three months, depending on climate and season. Once the root system is well developed, the cuttings can be transplanted into individual pots. The soil should first be soaked so as not to present any resistance when the cuttings are pulled ; this will avoid damaging the roots. The plants should then be repotted in garden soil to which a very small proportion of sand can be added.

Layering

This is an even simpler form of propagation. One of the lower branches of a mature plant is bent downwards and partially buried where it touches the ground. It can be held down either with a staple or simply by the weight of the earth on top of it. After a year the branch can be detached from the parent plant and transplanted elsewhere.

COLOUR COMBINATION AND FLOWER ARRANGEMENTS

A picture with unvarying, flat colours would seem lifeless ; the same applies to gardens and flower arrangements. What we have to do is to imitate the diversity of nature.

It is true that not all plants belonging to the same genus can be successfully combined together. A garden containing only a mixture of modern yellow, red, pink and orange roses would produce a feeling of distaste and excess. There is, however, no risk of this with the genus *Hydrangea*. Any number of different hydrangeas can be mixed together, and the result will never be off-putting. In fact, all hydrangeas contain the same vegetable pigment, which is present in different concentrations and gives a whole range of colours from the deepest purple to the palest blue, passing through different mauves, pinks and reds on the way. If you add all the different types of white, from the most green-tinged to the creamiest, then you have the whole hydrangea colour palette. Combine them however you like ; there is no danger of going wrong. On the contrary, you will automatically obtain a harmonious and lively effect.

Furthermore, the hydrangea is not an exclusive plant. Imitate nature and combine hydrangeas with a wide variety of other species ; the other species will be shown off to advantage, and so will the hydrangeas. The following illustrations may help to give you some ideas.

IDEAS FOR PLANT COMBINATION

		Illustration number
WHITE COLOUR :	*Hardy perennials and shrubs :*	
H. paniculata	Achillea, Abelia, Althea, Astilbe, Agapanthus	154, 155, 167
H. macrophylla	Campanula, Buddleia, Fuchsia	150, 156, 164
H. serrata	**Cortaderia**, Chelone, Galtonia	158
H. quercifolia	Gentiana, Gladiolus, Hemerocallis, Lychnis	166, 170
	Eryngium, Hosta, Lavatera, Malva	144, 145, 163
	Lobelia, Leycesteria, Phlox, Pulmonaria	148, 153, 162
	Polygonum, Rosa, Saponaria, Spiraea	143
	Climbers :	
	Clematis, Rosa	146, 147
	Bulbs and others :	
	Crinum, Crocosmia, Kniphofia, Iris, Lilium	159
BLUE, PINK AND RED COLOUR :	All the above, and also :	
H. macrophylla	**Achillea**, Cosmos, Digitalis	163
H. serrata	**Eupatoires**, Lysimachia, Lythrum	157, 163
H. involucrata	Lupinus, Hebe, **Sedum**	

TRIED AND TESTED COMBINATIONS :

H. arborescens 'Annabelle' and Spiraea 'Anthony Waterer'	
H. aspera 'Villosa', Acanthus spinosus	
H. m. 'Quadricolor' or 'Mouillère', Clematis 'Etoile Violette'	147
H. m. 'Libelle', Clematis heracleifolia 'Wyevale'	
H. m. 'Merveille Sanguine', Pulmonaria, Berberis 'Rose Glow'	152
H. pan. 'Grandiflora', Polygonum companulatum	143
H. pan. 'Unique', Berberis 'Rose Glow', Abelia, **Gypsophila**	
H. quercifolia., **Helichrysum 'Sulphur Light'**, Crocosmia	171
H. serrata 'Grayswood', Cosmos atrosanguineus	
H. sr. 'Preziosa', Buddleia 'White Cloud', **Sedum 'Autumn Joy'**	156

ARRANGEMENTS OF FRESH CUT FLOWERS : *Use the combinations* of plants suggested above.

ARRANGEMENTS OF DRIED CUT FLOWERS (For colour, see 'Cultivation' in volume 1).

Blues	H. macrophylla 'Altona', 'Europa', 'Hamburg', 'Rosea'
Purples	'Mme Travouillon', 'Renate Steiniger', 'Mathilde Gütges'
Whites	H. 'Mme Mouillère', 'Soeur Thérèse', 'Libelle'
Reds	H. 'Preziosa, 'Grayswood', 'Vorster Frührot', 'Sibilla'
Pinks	H. paniculata 'Pink Diamond', 'Burgundy Lace', 'Ruby'
	Combine them with the plants in bold type above.

Plus : Lunaria, Molucella, Anaphalis, Linum.

For Christmas : holly and skimmia berries and rosehips. Dried hydrangea flowers can also be "frosted" with an aerosol spray. Bluish conifers make an excellent background for this type of dried flower arrangement.

142. H. pan. 'Pink Diamond' & Sambucus 'Purpurea'

143. H. pan. 'Grandiflora' & Polygonum campanulatum

145. H. pan. 'Pink Wave' H. macr. 'Amethyst' & Hosta plant. 'Grandiflora'

144. H. ser. 'Grayswood' & Hosta plantaginea 'Grandiflora'

146. H. involucrata & Clematis x durandii

148. Hydrangeas & pulmonaria

147. 'Mme E. Mouillère' & Clematis 'Etoile Violette'

149. H. quercifolia & agave

150. 'Europa' & fuchsia

151. 'Bodensee'& Acer
dissectum 'Garnet'

152. 'Merveille
Sanguine' &
Berberis
'Rose Glow'

153. 'Merveille Sanguine' &
pulmonaria

155. 'Preziosa'
& Astilbe 'Fanal'

157. Various Hydrangeas
& Astilbe,Lupinus, Althaea

154. 'Blue Wave' & astilbes

156. 'Preziosa'
& buddleia

158. H. paniculata & Chelone

**159. H. quercifolia
'Snow Queen' & lily**

160. Hydrangea, Impatiens, Rosa glauca, purple beech.

161. H. aspera 'Kawakami' & butterfly V. Vulcain

162

163

164

162. Phlox
163. Lavatera
164. Buddleia
165. Achillea 'The Pearl', Digitalis, Lysimachia clethroides
166. Lychnis 'Alba'

165

166

167. H. paniculata & Agapanthus

168. H. paniculata & Lobelia

169. H. paniculata & japanese maple

170. H. pan. 'Brussels Lace'
hemorocalles 'Red Precious'

171. H. quercifolia 'Snow Flake' & Crocosmia, Oenothera

APPENDIX

TYPES OF INFLORESCENCES

lacecap

hortensia
or mop-head

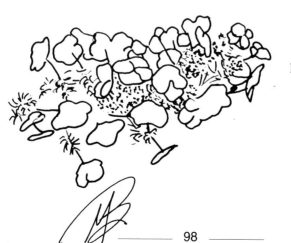

paniculate

INFLORESCENCE STRUCTURE

A. The different types of inflorescence.

Spherical or lacecap inflorescences have the structure of corymbs or cymes. Cone-shaped inflorescences in the form of panicles have the structure of compound clusters.

a. Cymes

1. Hortensia or mop-head type : found in the species *H. macrophylla* and *arborescens*. The inflorescence consists mainly of sterile florets with broadened sepals which resemble petals. The general shape is rounded or hemispherical.

2. Lacecap type : found in the species *H. serrata, macrophylla, aspera, arborescens, heteromalla, scandens, sikokiana* and *petiolaris*. The fertile flowers, which are tiny (a few millimetres in width and height), are present in the largest numbers, and are grouped together in the centre of the inflorescence, whose general shape is hemispherical. The central fertile flowers are surrounded by a row of very broad, coloured sterile florets in the form of a single or multiple coronet. There are sometimes a few sterile florets scattered amongst the fertile flowers.

3. Completely fertile type : *H. hirta* and *arborescens*. These two species mostly produce inflorescences in the form of hemispherical cymes consisting only of fertile flowers. There are, however, several cultivars of *H. arborescens* which produce sterile florets in greater or smaller numbers, in addition to the fertile flowers.

b. Panicles

4. Paniculate type : *H. paniculata* and *quercifolia*. These inflorescences are made up of a mixture of fertile flowers and sterile florets in compound clusters ; the overall shape of the inflorescences is roughly conical.

DIAGRAM OF THE STRUCTURE OF A
HYDRANGEA MACROPHYLLA INFLORESCENCE

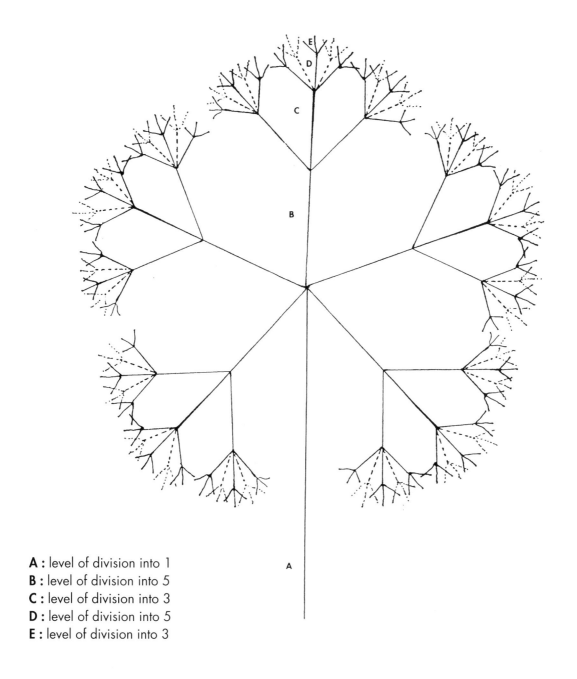

A : level of division into 1
B : level of division into 5
C : level of division into 3
D : level of division into 5
E : level of division into 3

B. The ramifications of the inflorescence

Within each species, the number of ramifications making up the inflorescence can be determined according to a diagram. The illustration opposite shows this type of structure for the *macrophylla* species, and will serve as an example to help understand the principle of describing inflorescences according to the number of ramifications. Starting from the stem, we obtain the sequence 1-5-3-5-3. The figure 1 represents the stem, and the following figures the number of ramifications at each level. The last figure is the number of pedicels (flower stalks). In some cases, the second-to-last level, instead of being divided further, becomes the single pedicel of a fertile flower.

Hydrangea serrata follows, more or less regularly, the structure of *H. macrophylla*, except for the number of pedicels, which is variable (2,3 or 5).

Hydrangea aspera has a different structure altogether, being divided into a pattern of equal pairs from the first to the last division, as follows : 1 (stem) - 2-2-2-2.

The pattern of division in *H. heteromalla* is rather erratic, although it is reminiscent of the pattern found in *H. macrophylla*.

In *H. paniculata*, the central stem remains undivided along the whole length of the inflorescence. The divisions, starting from the base and going towards the tip of the inflorescence, give the sequence 1-2-3-3-5, but, unlike hydrangeas with inflorescences of the corymb or multipartite cyme type, the pattern is repeated up to the tip of the inflorescence, giving the sequence 1 (stem) -2-3-3-5 - 1 (stem)-2-3-3-5 - 1 (stem)-2-3-3-5, and so forth. The pattern 1-3-3-3-5 is also found in some plants belonging to this species. Nevertheless, the further along one goes towards the tip the more "anarchic" the divisions become, and they end up by ignoring the pattern altogether Some cultivars which have been intensively worked on by breeders are almost completely anarchic.

The structure of *Hydrangea quercifolia* is itself almost completely anarchic, although there is a tendency in some cultivars to partially reproduce the pattern of *H. paniculata* (i.e. 1-2-3-3-5 or 1-3-3-3-5).

For all species, the pedicels (the final level) can terminate in either fertile flowers or sterile florets, depending on the cultivar or sub-species concerned, and on the position within the inflorescence of the first division to which the pedicels belong.

MUTATIONS

Mutations are as likely to be found in wild plants as in cultivated ones. There are many different conditions giving rise to these mutations, and the processes which cause them are still rather poorly understood.

A mutation is a modification in one or several parts of a plant, which is not the result of heredity.

Seed mutations
(changes in the embryonic DNA)

- Overexposure to sunlight

Excessive prolonged exposure of seeds to sunlight will bring about the death of most plants. The few survivors will have had their DNA modified by the action of ultra-violet rays. A few will reach maturity, but will be deformed. Plants with "double" or "triple" branches growing next to each other seem to be this type of mutant. Another mutation resulting from overexposure to sunlight is a form of dwarfism, often accompanied by various malformations[1].

Mutations in mature plants
(changes in the apical meristem)

- Exposure to a magnetic field, either underground (subterranean water) or overhead (high or medium voltage electricity lines).

Mutations of this type are extremely variable, and in most cases only affect the meristems at the tips of a few branches. They can, for example, take the following forms : flowers that are "double" or "triple" (or even more than triple) ; sterilised fertile flowers ; change in the colour of inflorescences, or even the disappearance of all colour apart from chlorophyll, resulting in green flowers ; bifid leaves, etc....
This type of mutation is often ephemeral, and does not reappear the next year.

- Deprivation of nutrients followed by an abundant supply of nutrients.

This also gives rise to a wide variety of mutations including, in certain cases, the variegation of the leaves of one or several branches[2]. These variegations can sometimes reappear in the following years. It is nevertheless unclear whether the variegated leaves are the direct result of deprivation of nutrients or whether, as another theory would have it, they are simply due to the fact that the poor state of health of the plant during its undernourished period renders it more susceptible to attack by some types of insect.

Mutations in mature plants are often transitory, but sometimes become fixed of their own accord. It is possible to artificially fix these mutations by means of plant propagation, although the processes dictating the success or failure of these experiments remain a mystery.

It should be stressed that, even in the wild, hydrangeas are plants that are particularly prone to the production of mutations. Convincing evidence will be provided by a visit to the plants' natural habitats, especially those of *Hydrangea macrophylla*.

---

1   "La Recherche" n° 256, July-August 1993. "Les rôles biologiques des couleurs florales" p.80.

2   "The Hydrangeas" by Michael Haworth-Booth, Fifth, revised edition, Constable, 1984.

GLOSSARY

(supplement to Volume 1)

Acuminate : Used to describe part of a plant whose tip tapers to a point.

Anthocyans : Natural plant colourings which give a range of colours from blue to red, passing through violet.

Apical : Relating to the apex, the tip or end of a part of a plant.

Award of Merit : A prize awarded to deserving plants by the Royal Horticultural Society (U.K.).

Bifid, trifid : Used to describe part of a plant divided or split into two (or three) parts or lobes.

Cyme : An inflorescence made up of a number of flowers carried on stems which are divided into branches underneath each flower. Each stem terminates in a single flower.

Denticulate : Edged with very small teeth.

Dimorphism : The existence of two clearly distinct forms of the same part within the same plant.

DNA : Deoxyribonucleic acid, the main constituent of chromosomes.

Double : Used to decribe flowers having more than the normal number of petals or sepals.

Filament : The stalk of a stamen.

Forcing : A horticultural technique whose aim is to obtain flowers outside the normal flowering season.

Hardy : Resistant to cold conditions.

Lanceolate : Narrow and tapering to a point, like the end of a spear.

Lenticel : A dot, generally coloured, on the surface of a branch, marking the presence of a tiny hole which allows the exchange of gases between the plant and the exterior.

Limb : The expanded, flat part of a leaf, not including the stalk.

Meristem : The growing tissue of a plant, that is capable of developing into different organs or tissues.

Pedicel : The small stalk attaching a flower to a ramification of an inflorescence.

Pubescent : Covered with short hairs resembling velvet.

Serrate : Edged with teeth which are turned towards the tip of the organ, like those of a saw.

Serrulate : Minutely saw-toothed.

Stoloniferous : Producing stolons, which are stems growing horizontally along the ground from the base of a plant, and from which new upright stems can grow.

INDEX

Note : The page numbers of illustrations are in bold type.
The page numbers of text are in normal type.

BIBLIOGRAPHY

(supplement to Volume 1)

Monographs :
Maillet, J.P. - L'hortensia : culture traditionnelle et miniaturisation, au travers des travaux du CNIH, 1987.
Meier, Fritz : - Tellerhortensien-Züchtungen, 1990.
Monnier, Jolinon, Lavondes, Elouard : - Philibert Commerson, 1993.
Moser Willy : - Haller, 75 Jahre Gärtnerei in Brugg, 1974.
Yamamoto, Takeomi : - Ajisai, 1979.
Yamamoto, Takeomi : - Ajisai-no-hanashi, 1981.
Yamamoto, Takeomi : - Ajisai-Hydrangea 1994.

Florae :
Satake, Hara, Watari, Tominari : Wild flowers of Japan, 1989.
Thunberg, Carl Peter : Flora Japonica, 1784.

Dictionaries :
Macmillan : - Botanical dictionary, 1992.
Belot, André : - Dictionnaire des arbres et arbustes des jardins, 1989.
Brickell, Christopher : - Grande Encyclopédie, Bordas, 1990.
Hay, Roy & Synge, Patrick-M : Dictionary of garden plants, Ebury, 1969.
Lemoine, E. (author of the article "Hydrangea") : - Le Bon Jardinier, 1947
Nicholson, G. : - Dictionnaire d'horticulture, 1893/94.

Miscellaneous :
Bullivant, Elizabeth : - Dried fresh flowers, 1989.
Hanoka, Yoshishige : - Hydrangea : shemino eng-gei, 1993.

Articles :
The Horticultural Trade Journal: - Portrait of Mr. L.R. Russell, 1925, 1956
Revue de l'Horticulture belge et étrangère : - 1878, 1900, 02, 03, 07, 08, 11, 12.
Bertrand, Hélène : - Arboretum d'Angers, Revue Horticole, n°316, 1991.
Bertrand,H., Becker,W., Eveleens,K.P. : - Cultivars, etc, Revue Horticole, n°313, 1992.
Burtt, B.L. : - Hydrangea integerrima, Curtis's
Botanical Magazine, June 1951.
De Belder, Robert : - Visit to Yakushima, I.D.S. Year Book, 1972.
Flore des Serres : - 1848, 1851, 1865, 1867, 1868, 1869, 1870.
Hendy, Jenny : - Shimmers in the shade, Gardens Illustrated, Aug/Sept. 1994
Hoshino, Mariko : - Hydrangeas at Varengeville s/mer, Fujingaho, May 1994.
Lancaster, Roy : - Hydrangea 'Snowcap', The Garden, July 1994.
Mallet, Corinne : - In search of Hydrangeas in Europe, The Hardy Plant, 1992.
Mallet, Corinne : - Hydrangea macrophylla 'Otaksa', The New Plantsman, September 1994.
Senouci, Heide : - Die schöne Hortensie, Mein Schöner Garten, July 1994.

Plant inventories :
APBF (France), 1976. - d'Andlau, 1993 - Boos, 1994. - Castle Howard, 1990 - Costin, 1989, 90, 91 - Dussine, 1994, - Eggins, 1990 - ENITHP, 1991 - Herkenrode, 1993 - Hillier's, 1991 - Jermyns, 1991 - Kalmthout, 1988, 1992 - Kerneur, 1994 - Lakeland, 1990 - Lullier, 1990 - Meise, 1992 - Minier, 1993 - Mount Congreve, 1991 - Renault, 1991 - Rosewarne, 1989 - Savill, 1992 - Siebold, 1846 - Thoby, 1993 - UPOV, 1990 - Vallet, 1993 - VanDusen, 1993 - Villa Taranto, 1963 - Vilmorin, 1904 - Waasland, 1991 - Wisley, 1992

Catalogues :
Barillet, 1913 - Bruant, 1906 - Centre d'Art Floral, 1978-1990 - Clibrans, 1958 - De Smet, 1861-79 - Draps, 1902 - Gauguin, 1902 - Gauntlett, 1950 - Haller, 1979-82 - Hartmann, 1908 - jubilé 1947 - Haworth-Booth, 1955 - Houry & Cassegrain, 1912 - Lemoine, 1904-1927 - Leroy, 1950 - Minier, 1964 - Minier & Halopé, 1912 - Mouillère, 1911-1931 - Mount Congreve, 1993 - Rivoire, 1914 - Rovelli, 1892-1911 - Russel, 1986, 1946 - Saitamaergei, 1914 - Slieve Donard, 1956 - Späth, 1906 - Steiniger, 50 Jahre, 1984 - Sunningdale, 1960 - Treseders, 1960 - 66 - Vangerre, 1845 - Siebold, 1846-1856-1861 - Wicks, 1963 - Witte, 1867.

HYDRANGEA NURSERIES

(supplement to Volume 1)

FRANCE

Pépinières MINIER (W)
49130 LES PONTS DE CE

Pépinières RENAULT (W)
Domaine du Rocher
53120 GORRON

Pépinières DAUGUET (R)
La Voisinière
53220 LARCHAMP

Pépinière du HAUT BOIS (R & W)
Alain DUSSINE
56800 TAUPONT PLOERMEL

ENGLAND

NUTLIN Nursery (R)
Crowborough Road
Nutley, near UCKFIELD, East Sussex
TN22 3HU

IRELAND

THE SEASIDE NURSERY (R)
Charles & Frieda DIJCK
Claddaghduff
Co.Galway

UNITED STATES

CAROLL GARDENS (R)
Alan L. Summers
444 East Main Street
PO BOX 310
WESTMINSTER
MD 21157

CORNELL FARM (R)
8212 SW
Barnes Road
PORTLAND
OREGON

COUNTRY GARDENS (R)
Keith Howe
2007 Federal Ave East
SEATTLE WA 98102

UNITED STATES

HERONSWOOD NURSERY Ltd (R)
Daniel Hinkley - Robert L. Jones
7530 288th Street NE
KINGSTON WA 98346

LOUISIANA NURSERY (R)
Albert, Dalton, Ken and Belle Durio
Route 7 Box 43.
OPELOUSAS LA 70570

MONROVIA Nursery (R)
Odry Thisdale
OREGON

WHITE FLOWER FARM (R)
Steve Frowine
PO BOX 50
Route 63, LITCHFIELD
CONNECTICUT 06759-0050

WOODLANDERS Inc (R)
Robert L.et Julia M Mackintosh
1128 Colleton Ave
AIKEN SC 29801

AUSTRALIA

Joan ARNOLD (W)
Buskers End
Saint Clair Street
BOWRAL NSW 2576

TOWNSENDS' Gardeners' Nursery (R)
Lot 4, Olinda-Monbulk Road
OLINDA 3788

ITALY

PIACENZA (R)
Mini Arboretum s.a.s.
di Guido Piacenza & C.
13057 POLLONE BIELLA

W : wholesale - **R** : retail

GARDENS AND COLLECTIONS TO VISIT
(supplement to Volume 1)

FRANCE

LES JARDINS DE BELLEVUE
76850 Beaumont le Hareng.

Alain DUSSINE
(by appointment only)
Pépinières du Haut Bois
56800 TAUPONT PLOERMEL

KERDALO
(by appointment only)
Prince Pierre Wolkonsky
Tredarzee 22220 Tréguier

LA MENITRE
La Grange Rouge
(Tuesdays and Fridays)
49250 LA MENITRE

PARC DE TREVAREZ
29520 Saint Goazec (Finistère)

PARC BOTANIQUE DE CORNOUAILLES
29120 Pont l'Abbé

PLANTARIUM de GAUJACQ
Jean Thoby
40330 Gaujacq

Le RAHIC
(by appointment only)
Pierre F. Michel-Kerneur`
56780 Ile aux Moines

SHAMROCK
Route de l'Eglise
76119 Varengeville s/mer
Guided visits by appointment
Tel: 35 85 14 64
from 15/07 to 15/11

JARDIN BOTANIQUE
du Château de Vauville
54440 - Vauville

CANADA

VAN DUSEN Botanical Gardens
5251 Oak Street
Vancouver BCV6M 4H1

SWITZERLAND

Centre Horticole LULLIER
Geneva (GE)

BASEL BOTANICAL GARDEN
Basel

IRELAND

John Joe COSTIN
(by appointment only)
Port Gloriam, Kilcock
Co. Kildare

CAPPOQUIN HOUSE
(by appointment only)
Cappoquin
Co. Waterford

GERMANY

MAINAU ISLAND
Bodensee

PHOTOGRAPHIC CREDITS

BY PHOTOGRAPHER

P. F. MICHEL-KERNEUR N°4. (author of "Ginkgo Biloba, l'arbre qui a vaincu le temps", Edition du Félin - 1985).

Fritz MEIER N°5,13, 31, 32, 41, 66.
(author of "Tellerhortensien Züchtungen" Flugschrift N°120 CH-8820 Wädenswil).

Corinne MALLET N°7, 10, 12, 30, 34, 51, 72, 81, 86, 88, 100, 101, 103, 104, 106, 107, 108, 111, 112, 116, 117, 118, 119, 120, 121, 122, 123, 124, 125, 126, 127, 128, 129, 130, 131, 132, 133, 134, 135, 136, 137, 138, 139, 140, 141, front cover.

Robert MALLET N°1, 2, 3, 6, 8, 9, 11, 14, 15, 16, 17, 18, 19, 20, 21, 22, 23, 24, 25, 26, 27, 28, 29, 33, 35, 36, 37, 38, 39, 48, 49, 50, 52, 53, 54, 55, 56, 57, 58, 59, 60, 61, 62, 63, 64, 65, 67, 68, 69, 70, 71, 73, 74, 75, 76, 77, 78, 79, 80, 82, 83, 84, 85, 87, 89, 91, 92, 93, 94, 95, 96, 97, 98, 99, 102, 105, 109, 110, 113, 114, 115, 142, 143, 144, 145, 146, 147, 148, 149, 150, 151, 152, 153, 154, 155, 156, 157, 158, 159, 160, 161, 162, 163, 164, 165, 166, 167, 168, 169, 170, 171, back cover.

BY PLACE

Le Cadran, 76150 Saint Jean du Cardonnay
N°109.

Ets. Dussine Paul, Chemin des Vieilles Carrières - 49000 Angers
N°22, 45, 47, 49, 52, 53, 56, 60, 61, 63, 68, 76, 77.

L'Etang de Launay, 76119 Varengeville s/mer
N°91.

Arboretum de Kalmthout, 2920 Kalmthout (near Antwerp)
N°158, 167, 168 (public).
N° 82, 86, 88, 105 (private).

Jardins Passion, 76230 Bois Guillaume
N° 151.

Les Jardins de Bellevue, 76850 Beaumont le H.
N°116.

Les Jardins d'Angélique, Montmain - 76520 Boos
N°164.

Parc des Moutiers, 76119 Varengeville s/mer
N°15, 115, 143, 154, 155, 169.

Jacques Nielz, 41100 Vendôme
N°38.

Le Rahic, 56780 Ile aux Moines
N° 4, 159.

Shamrock, 76119 Varengeville sur mer
N°1, 2, 3, 6, 7, 10, 11, 12, 17, 20, 21, 24, 26, 27, 28, 29, 30, 33, 34, 35, 37, 40, 42, 43, 44, 40, 42, 43, 44, 45, 46, 47, 48, 51, 52, 54, 55, 57, 59, 64, 65, 70, 71, 73, 75, 78, 80, 81, 84, 87, 89, 93, 94, 95, 96, 97, 98, 102, 112, 113, 142, 144, 145, 152, 153, 161, 163, 166.

Stourton House Garden -Mere - Wilts. U. K.
N°8, 23, 58, 62, 69, 148, 160.

Le Vasterival Ste Marguerite 76119 Varengeville sur mer
N°171.

Jardin Botanique du Château de Vauville, 54440 Vauville
N°149, back cover.

White House Farm - Ivy Hatch, Seal, Nr Sevenoaks, Kent, U. K.
N°14, 18, 19, 25, 74, 79, 99, 110, 114, 146, 147.

Varengeville s/mer 76119
N°156.

R.H.S. Garden Wisley -Surrey, U. K.
N°36, 170.

Yvonne de Vaucorbeil composed the flower arrangement in photo N° 159.

Computer equipment : Electrodom
76550 - Saint Aubin sur Scie

Photographic processing : Foci
Dieppe - Photovideo
76200 - Dieppe

Arka Laboratoire
52, rue Notre Dame des Champs
75006 - Paris

Technical supervision : Yves Patoux
18, rue Blaise Pascal
76100 - Rouen

Photogravure : Numéri'scann
129, rue Méridienne
76100 - Rouen

Photocomposition : Marché Conclu
31, rue Jean Ribault
76200 - Dieppe

Printed by
Imprimerie Féré
76150 - Maromme
November 1994

This book can be obtained directly from :

CENTRE D'ART FLORAL
Editions Robert MALLET
Route de l'Eglise
76119 - Varengeville sur mer
FRANCE

Tel. : 33.35.85.14.64 - Fax : 33.35.85.30.20